... zu sehen, dass die

Newtons Mechanik

von $\frac{q^2}{q_3}$

$$(28')$$

$$\frac{m}{2} q^2 + \dots$$

... Seite ist der geläufige ...

... Was bedeutet aber das ...

... gewinnen hier keine ...

... stante willkürlich ...

... dass dies Glied nicht ...

... verbunden ist. Mein ...

THEY MADE OUR WORLD

Five centuries of Great Scientists and Inventors

This book is based on
the BBC World Service series produced by
Sue Eadle.

© Original transcript material copyright
BBC World Service. Revised text copyright
Broadside Books Ltd.
2 Gurney Rd. London E15 1SH

ISBN: 0 951 5629 0 8

Design: 'The Studio',
Emma Axbey, Glen Coombes
15 Soho Square London W1
Picture Research: Diana Phillips, Patricia Robertson
Printed and Bound by Times Publishing, Singapore

CONTENTS

INTRODUCTION
by Dr. John Hamilton

Benjamin Franklin said that Man is the tool-making animal, and our world has been shaped by the human ability to control and modify our environment. Three hundred years ago everyday life for most people was not strikingly different from that of their parents or even their great grandparents, but beneath the surface a revolution was already gathering pace.

Since the beginning of the seventeenth century almost every aspect of our lives has been transformed by the increasingly rapid advance of technology, and the pace is still accelerating. The reason for this great explosion of change is that although chance still plays a part in many discoveries, we no longer depend entirely on trial and error. During this period technology became firmly linked to the parallel growth in our understanding of the world, provided by science. As new inventions such as the steam engine or microscope were developed they provoked as many questions as they answered, and provided the means to extend scientific investigation still further.

We will never know who made the great discoveries of ancient times, but the progress of the scientific and technological revolution of the last four hundred years has been well documented. The scientific "literature" is traditionally written in an impersonal way, concentrating only on the results of experiments and the conclusions drawn from them; but each major advance, even though it builds on the work of others, is the result of the creativity and intuition of individual men and women. Sometimes the ideas were very much "in the air" at the time, with several people racing towards the same breakthrough. It does not detract from Alexander Graham Bell's achievement, for example, that we would almost certainly have the telephone by now, even if he had kept to his original intention of teaching the deaf. We can only speculate, though, how different the progress of science and world history would have been without the creative genius of a man like Isaac Newton.

The series of twenty six programmes, first broadcast by the BBC World Service, presented a cross-section of the scientists and inventors who changed the way we live, and also how we look at the world. It is, of course, impossible to draw up a definitive list of the "greatest" pioneers in any field. Some, like Newton and Einstein are so important that they could not possibly be left out. Others, like Priestley or Turing, are less well known but made a contribution which was very influential in their time. The series begins with Francis Bacon, who was one of the first to describe how organised scientific enquiry could provide the knowledge which would give human beings the power to control their environment. The subsequent progress of science was spurred on mainly by a sense of wonder, the excitement of discovery and the desire to improve the condition of life. But the tree of knowledge gives power for both good and evil, and the series ends on a sombre note, with the team who developed of the first atomic bomb. The childhood of the human race had ended.

Dr. John Hamilton
London 1990

CHAPTER I

(1561 – 1626)
SIR FRANCIS BACON

The extraordinary scientific and technological achievements of our modern world are rooted in the intellectual ferment of the seventeenth century, "the century of genius". Until then, it was the philosophical ideas of the Greeks, Romans and church theologians which had largely dominated man's understanding of his universe; the concept of science, and scientific investigation, was not yet born.

THE CENTURY OF GENIUS
At the beginning of the seventeenth century, many believed that the world was flat with monsters waiting to devour those who ventured too far over the horizon; alchemists toiled hopelessly to turn base metals into gold, while men and women were still burned at the stake, accused of heresy or witchcraft. Within the space of one century, whole oceans and continents were discovered, and speculative kings would ponder the latest maps that were pushing back the frontiers of the unknown. With the invention of the telescope the heavens, too, were being re-mapped, and the medieval concept of the universe gave way to the revolutions of Copernicus, Kepler and Newton. Suddenly there was a desperate need for a new scientific approach which would organise this knowledge, and the man who did more than anyone else to establish this was Francis Bacon.

THE LITTLE LORD KEEPER
Francis Bacon was one of the great geniuses of the Elizabethan age. He was born into a life of culture and privilege, his father being the Lord Keeper of the Royal Seal at the court of Elizabeth. As a child, Francis had delighted the court with his serious and wise pronouncements, so much that Elizabeth would pat him on the head and call him her "Little Lord Keeper".

Francis Bacon had been destined for a glittering court life: at eighteen he had already accompanied ambassadors to France, and his uncle, Lord Burghley, was politically the most powerful man in England. But the early death of his father and political disgrace and execution of his eldest brother plunged the Bacon estate into debt and disarray. It was left to Francis to pay debts, comfort his by now deranged mother, and carve a future for himself. His friends at court largely fell away, and no advancement in any of the professions seemed possible. Although he was to struggle with debt all his life, his mind was already grappling with the problem of reorganising scientific investigation, which was to dominate his thinking until his death.

THE "GIGANTIC PLAN"

"I have taken all knowledge to be my province" wrote Bacon in 1592. He was living in an age of of exploration and discovery unequalled since the civilization of ancient Greece and Rome, but an age which was still bound by classical culture and thought. It was time for something new, rising to the challenge of the age.

In a Christmas entertainment for Queen Elizabeth in 1594, Bacon first analysed the intellectual problems confronting his generation, and suggested that royal assistance was necessary to solve them. He proceeded to unfold his extraordinary vision for the advancement of learning, a vision that would never leave him until his death. What Bacon proposed seems absolutely natural to us now, but it is only within the last one hundred and fifty years that his proposals became generally established. Four hundred years ago, Bacon's audience at the Christmas "device" could have hardly imagined anything so fantastical.

Bacon envisaged a vast library of books to be collected, in all known languages, as well as botanical gardens, a most comprehensive zoo, and a museum which would classify all inanimate objects and human inventions. Finally, a laboratory was necessary, furnished with "mills, instruments, furnaces and vessels, as may be a palace fit for a philosopher's stone", so that experimental research could be carried out. Only in this way could the heavens, the earth, the air, plants, animals, man, medicine and machinery be studied, observed and classified in a systematic way. Such a system would at last enable man to 'master' the mysteries of nature to his own advantage and profit.

Bacon impatiently dismissed the philiosphies of the ancients and theologians as blind and fruitless speculation, contributing nothing to man's advance:

"All the disputation of the learned never brought to light one effect of nature before unknown!"

THE BOOK, THE GUN AND THE 'NEEDLE'

According to Bacon, the three recent discoveries that had done more than any other to advance civilization dramatically, had been the printing press, gunpowder and the 'needle', or compass. But how haphazardly, he argued, had these inventions come about! If the existing learning of the ancients was reformed, rather than discarded, mankind could make great leaps forward. Learning would be harnessed to the needs of industry. In this way, the achingly slow progress of technological refinements by ordinary craftsmen, such as the development of tools or houses – could all be dramatically focussed, and speeded up.

While Elizabeth was flattered to be entertained by such an ingenious 'device', Bacon was politically out of favour with her, and had even been banished from court for a while. Also, like many of her courtiers watching the 'device' that day, the Queen was not inclined to take Bacon's ideas too seriously: they were, after all, presented as an entertainment. Although the sixty-one year old queen took great delight in the exploits of her explorers, or "sea-dogs" as she called them affectionately, she was now too old to prepare for the scientific revolution that would follow in their wake. Bacon realised he must bide his time, and work on the imagination and generosity of a younger monarch.

THE ADVANCEMENT OF LEARNING

By the time James I had acceeded to the throne, Bacon had temporarily dropped his political ambitions and devoted himself to his books instead. In 1605 he published *The Advancement of Learning,* and dedicated it to the new King. In it he elegantly and forcefully summed up all his former ideas: that it was vital to encourage the development of human knowledge, that all former knowledge which existed was not concerned with the direct engagement of the mind with the world around it, and was effectively useless in the new age that was dawning. Science was to be known by its fruits, not by endless theorizing: "Philosophy is like a statue. It draws admirers, but it cannot move." Consequently Aristotle's metaphysics were called "a tissue of cobwebs",

An engraving of Bacon on the frontispiece of the "Advancement of Learning" published in 1640.

while Plato was scorned as a "deluded theologian" and a "pompous poet". Finally, he demonstrated the possibilities for improving the sciences.

BACON AT COURT

Unfortunately, like Elizabeth, the King was not really stirred by Bacon's trumpet call for a new scientific approach. More conventional scholars of the day thought Bacon was a little mad, and kept a safe distance in case he entangled them in his schemes. In fact, he was

disliked and mistrusted by most of James' entourage. He was determined to please the king, however, and had an acknowledged genius for producing reams of draft documents and suggestions to improve the king's revenue. These streamed from his pen and were hopefully offered to James.

With his love of political organisation he also suggested early forms of the present ministries of agriculture, trade, finance, health and transport, to administer every aspect government, and encourage the introduction and development of manufacturing industries. This was too new for James, who was suspicious of any moves devolving governmental control out of his hands, and Bacon's proposals were largely rejected.

Bacon slowly ascended the political ladder, as far as was possible by sheer intelligence alone. His progress had always been hindered by his slight ineptness in friendships, coupled with a disdain of allying himself to any political faction. Bacon was unhappily aware of the need for court intrigue, but was extremely unsuited to it: whenever he resorted to a little necessary machiavellian behaviour, it usually back-fired and encouraged influential people to keep Bacon at greater arms-length than before. However, by 1617 he had become Lord Keeper, the same position that his father had held before his death, and by 1620 Bacon had attained the summit of his political career: the office of Lord Chancellor.

THE NOVUM ORGANUM

This triumph was celebrated by presenting to James his most ambitious and greatest work, intended as a blueprint for mankind's domination over nature, and written in Latin so that it might be understood by readers throughout Europe. The *Instauratio Magna*, or Great Instauration was a total reconstruction of sciences, arts, and all human knowledge.

In the first section he outlined six parts of his project in which man could regain his hold over nature. The second, and most famous section of his work was called the *Novum Organum*, which became so highly regarded by posterity that the whole work became known as the Novum Organum. The second section devoted itself to the invention of a new method of research, especially in the still undefined areas of biology, physics and chemistry. Mathematics had this essential part to play: "As physics, which advances farther and farther every day and develops new axioms, it will require fresh assistance from mathematics in many things."

He suggested the foundation of a "college of inventors", with pensions for research workers, allowances for travel and experiments, as well as libraries, laboratories and scientific prizes. In short, the whole status of science was to be raised higher than it had ever been before. This was all unheard of. Bacon proposed the whole venture should be financed by diverting funds from the foundation of more grammar

schools, which, in his opinion, were only fit for "breeding idle clerks", and had earmarked several old, rich and single nobles whose fortunes might be put to such good use. The gentlemen in question not unnaturally felt their fortunes were their own affairs, and one or two had quite a struggle to extricate themselves from Bacon's glorious plans.

SCIENCE AND THE SPHINX

Inspired by his great idea, Bacon urged men to rid their minds of "idols", that is, fixed ideas and false notions that have become so rooted that they obstruct any new thinking:

"If a man will begin with certainties, he will end in doubts; but if he will be content with doubts, he shall end in certainties."

Patiently explaining to his slower audience, he used fables to illustrate his point. He described the need for the scientist to have great patience while he collected and dissected evidence, and wrote that the footsore Oedipus was only able to solve the riddle of the sphinx by thinking long and hard as he limped along. The sphinx represented the mysteries of science, and limping Oedipus the slogging human scientist.

The *Instauratio Magna* was dedicated to James I, who was solemnly presented with the first copy. He accepted it graciously and even soldiered on to read it to the end, but obviously found it quite a chore, sighing that it was like "the peace of God, in that it passeth all understanding . . . " A copy presented to Coke, Bacon's lifelong political rival, had a much chillier reception. Coke sourly wrote on the title page: "You propose to reconstruct the teaching of wise men of old. Reconstruct first our laws and justice."

However, it was James' response that primarily concerned Bacon, and that turned out to be sufficiently polite and encouraging to delight him. Bacon immediately tried to persuade the King to finance the book's recommendations, and felt that his star was at its zenith. The following year James created him Viscount St. Albans, and it seemed that at last he had achieved the success and acceptance he had always desired.

DISASTER

Meanwhile, Bacon had been making himself extremely unpopular by supporting state monopolies, in which

The frontispiece from the History of the Royal Society, *published in 1667. It shows Charles II crowned with laurels as the royal patron, and Bacon in the foreground.*

profits from certain manufactures would go straight to the King or his favourites. Although Bacon was privately against monopolies, his support for James' pressing need to finance his European wars overran all caution.

Both Bacon and Coke considered monopolies to be legal, while in practice they were so unpopular that they could only be enforced through a complex system of bribes. The monopoly which created the greatest uproar was the manufacture of gold and silver thread. Bacon considered that bullion was the lifeblood of the state, and far too significant and precious to be left to the use of artisans in a free market. He drafted a patent giving the family of Buckingham, the King's favourite, the bulk of the profits. There was an uproar among the city business men, especially after it was discovered that bullion from the treasury had been melted to swell the proceeds. Other highly unpopular patents followed, until the outraged Commons demanded an inquiry of the King. Charges of corruption against Bacon's Court of Chancery flew in all directions, and finally, to his astonishment, Bacon was charged with accepting bribes. He was unable to deny the charges, and with sickness and heavy heart was compelled to resign the great position of which he had been so proud:

"By the King's great favour I received the Great Seal, by my own great fault I lost it."

In accordance with the standards of the day, Bacon had not acted with any great irregularity. But it was unfortunate that on the same day he had instructed judges to ". . . fly all bribery and corruption, and preserve your integrity", he had also accepted a purse of £100 from one of his own litigants.

In the days of Elizabeth, it was accepted that statesmen such as the great Lord Burghley would take gifts in return for patronage and favours at court. This was the atmosphere in which Bacon had grown up; moreover, statesmen were only paid token salaries and were expected to maintain their magnificent entourages through family wealth. Bacon had none of this; and in the intervening forty years the climate had changed. A rising class of business men were determined to fight for changes in parliamentary procedure so that matters concerning finance and commerce were increasingly settled under their influence in the House of Commons, rather than by the monarch. The issuing of unfair monopolies and patents, and the acceptance of bribes to favour one litigant over another, were quickly becoming outdated practices. In this respect, Bacon had fallen victim to the changing times he had been preparing for through his life's work.

OBSCURITY AND DEATH

Although Bacon was rapidly pardoned, he was forced into retirement. He seemed quite resigned to his fate, and withdrew into himself to devote time to his beloved studies. The problem of heat had absorbed him, and he even proposed the now accepted idea that heat was conducted by molecules in motion. In March 1926 as his carriage was driving through the snow of Highgate village north of London, he was suddenly struck with an idea about the possibilities of snow as a preservative, which he wanted to test. He leapt from the carriage, bought a chicken from a farmer's wife, and gutted it on the spot, stuffing it with snow to test his theory. Unfortunately he caught a serious chill in the process from which he never recovered, and died the following month, his debts vastly outstripping his assets.

THE STATESMAN OF SCIENCE

Bacon was far ahead of his contemporaries in his plans for state-sponsored scientific research: even today, the science departments of most universities are barely a hundred years old. Although his life had forced him into the roles of courtier, politician and judge, all of which he adopted uneasily, his greatest delight had been the organisation of science. Many of his theories and investigations were on the wrong track, and he had notoriously dismissed the theories of Galileo, as well as ignoring the famous contemporary biological investigations of Harvey.

His life's work had not been entirely frustrated. He had certainly succeeded in raising the status of science, although not yet as high as he would have wished. He had also hoped to fund a scientific chair at the universities of Oxford or Cambridge, but his estate was too depleted for that. However, under James he had founded the Royal Society which would attract the foremost scientists of his and future ages, and so begin the great work he had always envisaged. After Bacon's death, his reputation grew rapidly, and his great vision for the role of science in modern society is one that still remains to be completed.

CHAPTER II

(1643 – 1727)
SIR ISAAC NEWTON

Of the twenty-six great scientists and pioneers in this book Isaac Newton and Albert Einstein stand out above the others like high peaks in a range of mountains. Both tackled some of the same fundamental problems of physics – and both changed the way in which we look at the world of matter and energy. By any standards Newton was a mighty genius and his greatest work, on the laws of motion and the theory of gravitation, set a pattern for science for the next three hundred years. It was Isaac Newton who gave the first, and definitive explanation of how the universe worked, from the smallest particles to the stars and galaxies.

A MATHEMATICAL PRODIGY

Isaac Newton was born into a humble farming family living at Woolsthorpe, a village near Grantham, in Lincolnshire. His father died before he was born and he grew up, as a rather weakly child, under the care of his mother and grandmother. His uncle, the Reverend William Ayscough, was the first person to recognise that he was exceptionally gifted. On his advice the young Isaac was sent to Grantham Grammar school, rather than helping to run the family farm. It is said that as a boy he was fascinated by making mathematical models and such things as sundials and a working windmill, but unfortunately none of these have survived.

In 1661, when he was eighteen, he entered Cambridge University as an undergraduate but, as he came from a poor family, he had to help support himself by waiting at table in the college. He soon established a reputation as a brilliant mathematician and was elected a Fellow of Trinity College. In 1668, while still only twenty-seven, he was appointed Professor of Mathematics, a post which he held for over thirty years. His importance as a scientist was also soon recognised and in 1672 he became a Fellow of the Royal Society. He remained a very active member throughout his life and in 1703 became President. He was the first scientist to be awarded a knighthood.

There is no guarantee that someone with such a breadth and depth of intellectual vision can apply this to his own life, and it must be admitted that, as a person, he could be very difficult. Newton acknowledged his debt to others – in general terms – in a letter to Robert Hooke:

"If I have seen further it is by standing on the shoulders of giants".

'FEARFUL, CAUTIOUS AND SUSPICIOUS'

This apparent humility was not always shown in his relations with particular scientists and mathematicians of the time, especially if there was any question about sharing the credit for his ideas; and his Cambridge contemporaries spoke of his "fearful, cautious and suspicious temper". His most acrimonious dispute was with the German mathematician Leibniz. Both men, quite independently, developed that important branch of mathematics which Newton called fluxions and which we now call calculus. Although Newton may have discovered the ideas of calculus first, Leibniz published his work earlier. Newton conducted a long and vitriolic campaign against him and shamelessly used his influence with the Royal Society to have Leibniz condemned, quite unjustly, as a plagiarist. Sadly, his later years were often clouded by such disputes, made even more bitter when others joined the battle on one side or the other.

Fortunately Newton's place in the scientific pantheon depends not on his qualities as a person but on his genius for harnessing this tenacity and single mindedness in laying the foundations of modern physics.

His own description of how he achieved his results was: "by thinking on it continually", and in fact he often concentrated so intensely on the work in hand that he forgot to eat his meals or to go to bed. Newton, like Sherlock Holmes, gained his main satisfaction from solving problems, almost as an intellectual game. Once he had seen the solution clearly he was restless to move on to something else and grudged the time spent writing in order to share his work with others. (Some of his enemies interpreted this as a deliberate withholding of information).

PRINCIPIA MATHEMATICA

The main outlines of his theories were all developed during his early years in Cambridge, much of the work being crowded into the two years of 1664/65. At this time the great plague made it necessary to close the university and Newton found himself once again living in the isolated family home, with plenty of time to think and to carry out experiments. But it took him another twenty years to complete a full account. The delay was partly caused by another of his bitter quarrels, this time with Robert Hooke who claimed that he should share the credit for the discovery of the universal law of gravitation. But here Newton was certainly in the right; he had completed his calculations in 1666, long before Hooke's work, and his theory was far more comprehensive than anything envisaged by Hooke. After much urging from his friend Halley, he got down to the task of drawing together all his work on mechanics and gravitation. In 1686 he finally published, at Halley's expense, the three great books which make up Philosophiae Naturalis Principia Mathematica, usually known as The Principia.

ON THE SHOULDERS OF GIANTS

The first book of The Principia deals with the motion of bodies, and here we have one of those decisive changes in the way we look at the world, – not so much at the details, but at the overall picture. It was a change of paradigm, which finally replaced the ideas that had formed the basis of scientific thought for two thousand

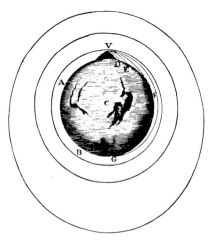

Newton's diagram showing what happens to an object launched from a mountain at different speeds. The same laws of gravity also determine the movement of the planets.

A. *absolute Gravity.* B. *Conatus against absolute Gravity.* C. *partial Gravity.*
D. *comparative Gravity* E. *horizontal, or good Sence.* F. *Wit.* G. *comparative Levity*
or Coxcomb. H. *partial Levity, or pert Fool.* I. *absolute Levity, or Stark Fool.*

A contemporary cartoon satirizing Newton's Laws of Gravity, with figures ranging from (A) Absolute Gravity to (I) Absolute Levity.

years since the time of Aristotle. The older ideas were not based on anything we would recognise as experimental evidence, although in many respects they followed what seemed to be a commonsense, everyday experience of the world. According to Aristotle, motion must either be natural or imposed. If left to itself, a moving object gradually slows down – unless we artificially keep it moving by pushing it. It is natural for a heavy object, such as a rock, to roll downhill and equally natural for fire and smoke to leap upwards to their proper place high in the atmosphere. These changes, like all things on earth, eventually come to an end. The heavens provided a complete contrast and seemed to obey entirely different laws. The sun, moon and stars appear to circle around the earth with unceasing movement, and the circle (with no beginning or end) was their natural form of motion. Physics seemed to reflect and reinforce the teachings of religion, contrasting the imperfect, transient earth with the perfect unchanging heavens.

(Galileo still retained the belief that the heavenly bodies must move in perfectly circular paths. Even Kepler had to struggle hard before he could accept the conclusions forced on him by his own work on the movements of the planets, work which formed an essential basis for Newton's gravitational theory).

NEWTON AND GRAVITY

Our everyday experience does not conflict with Aristotle's ideas, which is one reason why they held the field for so long. Even today many people would feel in their bones that a heavy object, such as a lead weight, must fall faster than a lighter object – as Aristotle's ideas required. It was Galileo who first tested the evidence on this. Despite the stories about him timing the fall of objects that he dropped from the leaning tower of Pisa, it was not easy for Galileo to make the precise measurements required, because of the limitations of the instruments available to him. However, by slowing down the fall, in fact by measuring the movement of balls rolling down a smooth slope, Galileo was able to show that Aristotle had been wrong and that, if we allow for air resistance, all objects fall at the same rate. (This was strikingly shown in one of the transmissions from the moon, when a feather and a coin were dropped -and, in the airless conditions of the moon, they were seen falling at the same speed). Galileo's experiments, and Newton's conclusions from them, stood the older ideas on their head: instead of asking what keeps an object moving, it was now clear that a moving object ought to keep moving with a steady velocity unless it is affected by some external influence.

NEWTON'S LAWS OF MOTION

This concept of inertia, was refined in Newton's First Law of motion. Once we recognise the idea, we can find many examples around us. When we apply the brakes of a car it does not stop instantly, and if we brake very hard the passengers carry on moving at the original speed of the car until they hit the windscreen, unless restrained by seat belts. This is because they, like everything material, have inertia, and will continue moving in a straight line with a constant velocity unless or until some outside force acts to stop them.

Newton's Second Law is concerned with the measurement of force, and says that the speed of an object changes in proportion to the amount of force acting on it. Again, this seems almost obvious once the idea has been formulated: if you are on a flat road, the harder you pedal a bicycle the faster it will go!

We can state this as a simple mathematical expression:

$$F = m.a$$
$$\text{Force} = \text{Mass} \times \text{Acceleration}$$

(The unit by which force is measured has been named after Newton – and, by a happy coincidence, the force of gravity on an apple is about 1 Newton)!

The Third Law states: "To every action there is always imposed an equal reaction. Whatever draws or presses another is as much drawn or pressed by that other. If you press a stone with your finger, the finger is also pressed by the stone".

At first sight, this looks a less familiar idea but there are some circumstances where this idea is clearly involved. For example, when a rifle is fired the bullet speeds off in one direction, but the gun kicks back in the opposite direction. This is also the way that a rocket is propelled through empty space – the action of the gases rushing away from it as the fuel burns causes the rocket to move in the opposite direction by reaction.

THE MOVEMENTS OF APPLES – AND GALAXIES

Newton's theory of universal gravitation, like the laws of motion, builds on the work of others, especially Galileo and Kepler. The inspiration that prompted his theory has passed into the folklore of science history:

"After dinner, the weather being warm, we went into the garden and drank tea under the shade of some apple trees, only he and myself. Amidst other discourse, he told me he was in just the same situation as when formerly the notion of gravitation came into his mind. It was occasion'd by the fall of an apple, as he sat in contemplative mood. Why should that apple descend perpendicularly to the ground, thought he to himself? Why should it not go sideways or upwards, but constantly to the earth's centre? Assuredly the reason is that the earth draws it. There must be a drawing power in matter: and the sum of the drawing power must be in the earth's centre, not in any side of the earth. Therefore does this apple fall perpendicularly or towards the centre.

Newton's reflecting telescope which he constructed in 1668.

Therefore the apple draws the earth, as well as the earth draws the apple. That there is a power, like that we call gravity, which extends itself thro' the universe."

In this way, gravity binds the universe together and firmly unites the earth with the heavens, finally bringing them under the same laws. His theory went far beyond the sort of general intuition that had already occurred to others, especially Kepler and Hooke. Physicists consider this to be Newton's crucial leap forward. To link the calculations of planetary movement to observations of those movements required a highly elaborated mathematical theory. It was quite a jump from the superficial assertion of contemporary scientists, that "bodies attract each other, and this attraction weakens as they get further apart."

OF TIDES AND COMETS

It is the mark of a great theory that it does not just explain the evidence on which it was based, but also links together and provides an insight into other things so far unexplained, and apparently quite unconnected. Newton was able, for the first time, to give a full explanation of the tides. The earth attracts the moon, and prevents it from flying off into space; but the moon pulls on the earth as well, causing the oceans to bulge out slightly towards it, so producing the tides. The strength of this gravitational pull will depend on how much matter is present, and how far away it is. The sun is vastly greater than the moon, and holds all of the solar system in its gravitational grip but, because it is so much further away from us than the moon, its effect on the oceans is much smaller. Newton was therefore able to explain that the tides will be highest at those times in the month when the sun and moon are in line and pulling together to produce the "spring" tides; and that the lowest or "neap" tides will ocur when the sun and moon are pulling at right angles to each other.

Newton also showed that those mysterious intruders, the comets, were material bodies acted upon by the same forces as the planets, and like them members of the solar system orbiting around the sun. His friend Edmund Halley was able to apply Newton's theory to connect the comet, which he discovered in 1682 (and which is named after him), with earlier reports of comets in 1531 and 1607 – and to predict that it would reappear after another 75 years.

Newton was even able to imagine the possibility of artificial satellites, which once put into orbit around the earth would: "go on revolving through the heavens in those orbits just as the planets do in their orbits."

It was almost three hundred years before Sputnik was launched and technology finally caught up with Newton's imagination.

HYPOTHESES NON FINGO

Newton was careful to distinguish those parts of science where he considered there was sufficient experimental evidence to put forward a sound theoretical explanation, and he refused to be drawn into speculations which went beyond the evidence – or in his own words: "Hypotheses non fingo". (Like others at that time, Newton kept to the tradition of publishing his major works in Latin).

Despite the great sweep of his theory of gravitation, in one important respect it remained incomplete: it contained no clue about *how* bodies attracted each other, or the mechanism by which this force was transmitted through millions of miles of empty space. This "action at a distance", without any physical connection between the bodies, conflicted with the approach of Descartes and this delayed the acceptance of

White light broken up by a prism into the colours of the rainbow, as described by Newton in The Optiks *of 1704.*

Newton's ideas in France for many years. The nature of gravity must have teased Newton throughout his life, but he remained true to his principle of staying on the solid ground of known facts.

NEWTON'S STUDY OF LIGHT

Newton never lost his childhood facility for making things and one achievement of which he was very proud was designing a new type of telescope that used a curved mirror to gather the light instead of a lens. (Nearly all of the great telescopes used in astronomy today are of this type). In 1668 he built two of these "Newtonian reflectors" with his own hands, and they created great excitement. Diagrams were sent to other scientists in Europe, such as Huygens, and the telescope was demonstrated to King Charles II. It was largely a result of the interest in this important invention that Newton was admitted to the Royal Society in 1672.

The great success of Newton's theoretical work on mechanics and gravitation has tended to overshadow the contributions he made to other aspects of science; but his design of the new telescope grew out of an important study of light. In 1704 he published his other major work, *The Optiks*, dealing with the conclusions from his many experiments in this field since his early years in Cambridge. One of the most important things he had discovered was that white light could be broken up into a spectrum of colours by passing it through a prism – and that coloured light could be recombined to give white. For example, "Newton's disc" is a circular card painted, in sections, with the colours of the spectrum. When spun like a top, the colours merge together to give a dull white appearance. He also investigated the way that colours are produced by thin films of liquids, for example in soap bubbles and patches of oil floating on water, or when a thin layer of air is trapped between two pieces of glass ("Newton's rings").

At this time, and for many years afterwards, there was a dispute about the nature of light; whether it was a stream of minute particles ("corpuscles") bouncing off the illuminated object, or a wave motion, as proposed by Newton's contemporary, Huygens. From the results of his investigations Newton came down on the side of the "corpuscular theory". But by the early nineteenth century the wave theory appeared to have won the day, and Newton's important contributions to the study of light may have been rather obscured because, for once, he was on the losing side. From the viewpoint of the twentieth century, however, the issue is not as clear cut, and in a sense Newton and Huygens were both right.

ISAAC NEWTON M.P.

In 1685 Newton was put on a parliamentary committee to investigate the religious credentials of those wishing to study or teach at the English universities. At the time Cambridge became involved in a controversy when a Catholic priest was refused admission. King James II, who was also a Catholic, tried to persuade the university to reverse its decision. Newton's strongly Protestant views helped to tip the balance and the king's demand was refused. As a result of this forray into the politics of the time, Newton was elected in 1688 as Member of Parliament for Cambridge University.

OLD AGE

By the time he was fifty his main creative work in science was finished. Not long after the publication of the Principia he suffered a mental breakdown, but by 1693 he had recovered and had another thirty-four years of

public service, with only an occasional return to scientific matters. In 1696 he was made Warden of the Royal Mint, a post he held while still retaining his position as professor of Mathematics for a further seven years. His interest in chemistry, and especially the knowledge of metals he had gained while making the mirrors for his telescopes, fitted him well for this post. In 1703 he gave up the chair of mathematics and became Master of the Royal Mint, gaining greater leisure to supervise the publication of his works – and also finding a new outlet for his "suspicious temper", by hunting down and prosecuting counterfeiters with ferocious zeal. With the security of this position he settled down to a comfortable life as he reached old age. He had never married and was now looked after by his niece, assisted by six servants. He was rather stout man with long wavy hair, now silver – still a formidable foe to his enemies, but generous and hospitable to his circle of friends. From his eightieth year he became increasingly frail, and he died in 1727 at the age of eighty five. He was buried with fitting ceremony in Westminster Abbey. Alexander Pope wrote the well known lines, intended as his epitaph:

"Nature and Nature's laws lay hid in night:
God said 'Let Newton be!' and all was light."

Over the two centuries following his death, Newton's approach was extended successfully to many other aspects of science; indeed, the sweep of his ideas was so great it that seemed to many scientists of the nineteenth century that, in principle, the whole of science was understood. Nature behaved as a great machine, running smoothly according to the laws of motion and gravitation – all that remained was for the last details to be filled in. That this picture, in its turn, had to be extensively revised is no criticism of Newton and certainly does not diminish his importance. Even with the adjustments that came during this century with Einstein's theory of relativity, Newton's laws still form the bedrock of ordinary physics today.

We should, though, leave the last word to Newton:
"I do not know what I may appear to the world, but to myself I seem to have been only like a boy playing on the sea-shore, and diverting myself in finding a smoother pebble or a prettier shell than ordinary, whilst the great ocean of truth lay all undiscovered before me."

CHAPTER III

(1733 – 1804)
JOSEPH PRIESTLEY

By the beginning of the Eighteenth century, physics had already been put on a sound theoretical foundation, especially through the work of Isaac Newton (Chapter II); but in chemistry so many of the essential pieces of the jigsaw were missing that it was still difficult to see even the beginnings of a clear picture. Priestley's contribution to the development of science was to discover some of these key pieces, although it was left to others to draw out the full conclusions from his work.

PRIESTLEY THE NON-CONFORMIST

Joseph Priestley was born at Fieldhead, near Leeds, and grew up in a deeply religious family, becoming a man of strong convictions but with an open, inquiring mind. His views on religious doctrines drew him away from his original Calvinist faith and he trained for the ministry of the Unitarian church. As a non-conformist, Priestley was cut off from the traditional educational institutions, which were still open only to members of the Church of England, but this did not prove to be a disadvantage to him. The Dissenters had set up their own academies and these gave a much greater emphasis to practical subjects, and were the first schools to include subjects such as history, economics and natural science in their curriculum. This made them attractively 'modern', and they drew pupils from a wide circle, especially from the expanding middle class.

Priestley spent several years teaching in the academy at Warrington, and it was here that he first became interested in chemistry and started to carry out his own experiments. His enthusiasm for science was increased further by meeting the Anglo-American Benjamin Franklin and discussing with him the new developments in electricity. Like other non-conformists of his time, Priestley found no conflict between his interest in science and his religious faith; to the contrary, science was seen as another means of revealing the works of the Creator. Priestley believed in the idea of 'Necessity', as he called it. The natural world was what it was because God had made it that way, which made it all the more fascinating for Priestley to study.

THE LUNATICS

For the greater part of his life Priestley was based in the Midlands, in the towns which were growing rapidly in size and importance with the developing Industrial Revolution. In Birmingham he became a member of the Lunar Society (sometimes known as the "lunatic society"). It was so called because they met monthly at full moon, to make it easier to find their way home at the end of the evening. This was an informal discussion group which included many other keen amateur scientists and also some of the leaders of the new

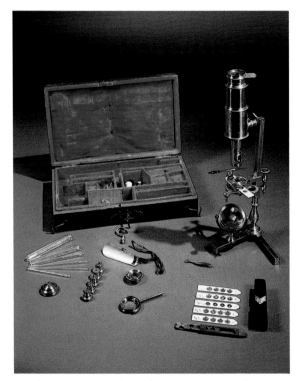

Priestley's microscope at the London Science Museum, showing different sizes of slides.

industries who were beginning to apply science and technology, including men such as Wedgwood and James Watt (Chapter XIII). Science was still to a large extent a private interest, and the results of experiments might remain in the notebooks of the scientist for many years before being published, if at all, in a book of his collected work. So the meetings of such groups and learned societies around the country played an important part in spreading information about discoveries and new techniques; the published "proceedings" which gave reports of the lectures and discussions, were the forerunners of the scientific journals that later became the standard means of sharing information (and establishing priority) among scientists.

Priestley made the first of his major scientific discoveries in 1766, during experiments on electrically charged bodies. He found that the strength of the attraction or repulsion between them dropped away with the their distance apart. But, as with his better known work on oxygen, he did not appreciate the full significance of his discovery – and in this case, too, it was a French scientist (Coulomb) who worked out the full implications of his work.

In 1772 Priestley moved to Leeds to take up the ministry of Mill Hill chapel. Close to his house there was a brewery, and this was to provide both an opportunity and a further spur for his interest in chemistry. Here he began an important series of experiments on the gas we now call carbon dioxide, which was produced in large quantities as part of the fermentation process.

AIRS AND GASES

At this time only two gases were known, apart from ordinary air: carbon dioxide and hydrogen. Even these were still seen as varieties of air, rather than as distinct substances in their own right. (Hydrogen was known as "inflammable air" and carbon dioxide as "fixed air"). One of the problems that had held back progress was the practical difficulty of handling gases, which disperse rapidly and mix with the air unless they can be collected and kept in a closed container. Few of the earlier investigators had fully realised the problem, or worked out satisfactory techniques to overcome these difficulties and so, unlike liquids and solids, the gases were still almost an unknown territory. "Pneumatic chemistry" was to play a crucial role in the development of

Experiment with the Air Pump *by Joseph Wright of Derby (1737-1797) showing an early investigation into 'dephlogisticated' air.*

chemistry during the next few years.

About ten years earlier Joseph Black had carried out some pioneering work on "fixed air". He had never actually isolated carbon dioxide but he demonstrated, for the first time, that when the gas was set free from chalk, the weight of the chalk decreased; and also that a certain weight of this gas was always "fixed" in a given amount of chalk. This was an important step towards recognising gases as true substances which could be weighed and measured. Priestley may have heard something of Black's work before starting his own investigations. It is known, for example, that Black corresponded with James Watt who was, with Priestley, a member of the Birmingham Lunar Society.

THE INVENTION OF SODA WATER

Soon after his arrival in Leeds Priestley set up a simple laboratory with apparatus which, although home-made, already represented a considerable advance over previous practice. To collect the carbon dioxide he used a wooden washing tub filled with water as a "pneumatic trough". For containers he used glass jars and bottles, which he filled with water and held upside down over the tub so as to lead the gas into them through a tube.

Priestley identified the gas produced during fermentation as the "fixed air" that had been investigated by Joseph Black. One of the new things he discovered about it was that carbon dioxide dissolves easily in water under pressure – and that the result tastes quite pleasant: he had invented soda water! (As Priestley often spoke out against the evils of alcohol, he might have been disturbed had he known how much this discovery would later be appreciated by whisky drinkers.)

Armed with these new techniques he went on to discover ten new "airs". One important modification that he made to his original apparatus was to collect the gases over mercury instead of water. This allowed him to isolate for the first time gases such as "spirit of salt" (hydrogen chloride) and ammonia, which are far too soluble to be collected over water. Other gases which he isolated for the first time included two of the oxides of nitrogen, sulphur dioxide and, in 1774, by far the most important, oxygen itself. There is some doubt whether he was, in fact, the first person to discover oxygen. Certainly the Swedish chemist Carl Scheele (who was the first person to discover chlorine) could claim equal credit; both men were working entirely independently and along rather different lines. Both recognised that they had made an important discovery, but neither was aware of the full significance of this new gas or the effect that its discovery would have on the currently accepted theory of combustion.

THE PHLOGISTON THEORY

If we watch wood or coal burning we see flames leap out from it, and the original material is clearly converted into something simpler, the ash. It is not difficult to see how the process of combustion was misunderstood: such common observations were taken by the alchemists as evidence that all materials which burn must contain a "flammable principle". This was linked with the old idea of the four "elements"; earth, air, water and fire; and a material, when it burns, was thought to be breaking up into its component elements.

The idea that something is expelled from a burning material was elaborated in 1669 by Johann Becher, a professor of medicine. This was developed further by Becher's pupil Georg Stahl, who renamed the flammable principle "phlogiston" and put forward a new theory, which was to hold the field for a century.

The phlogiston theory survived for so long because, although it was almost exactly the opposite of the truth, it appeared to give an explanation for a wide range of important chemical processes. For example, according to Stahl, a metal was composed of two parts: a "calx", or ash, combined with phlogiston. When it was burned the phlogiston was released, leaving behind the calx. If this ash was heated with a substance rich in phlogiston, such as carbon, the theory correctly predicted that the metal would be re-formed. The theory also explained why a volume of air could only support a certain amount of combustion: once the air had become saturated with phlogiston, it could take up no more. Even the awkward observation that tin gained in weight when it was heated was accomodated by assuming that phlogiston possessed 'levity', the opposite to weight, and therefore buoyed up the metal so that it appeared to weigh less than its calx. Perhaps the main benefit of the theory was that it provided a new language for discussing chemistry as a science, marking a decisive break from the earlier ideas of the alchemists.

To the end of his life Priestley continued to use the old theory for discussing and explaining his work on gases and always referred to his greatest discovery as "dephlogisticated air" rather than oxygen. All his life, Priestley had preferred to press on with his experiments, rather than worrying too much about the theories behind them. Perhaps it was for this reason that Priestley clung to the theory, even after the work of Lavoisier (Chapter IV), and failed to appreciate that his own work had sounded the death knell for phlogiston.

THE DISCOVERY OF OXYGEN

Priestley's work on gases naturally led him to take a close interest in the part played by the air in combustion and respiration. He carried out many experiments in which, for example, a mouse or a lighted candle was confined in a container standing over water or mercury. In both cases the air was reduced in volume and what was left was no longer able to support either life or combustion. From this he understood that both combustion and respiration were essentially the same chemical process, and that the air played a part in both. He also showed that plants can restore the air, and that light plays an essential part in this process.

His most famous experiment was once again "made

An etching of 1775 showing Priestley's apparatus for his experiments on gases.

casually" and is a fortunate example of his tendency not to speculate too much about theory. In fact according to the phlogiston theory nothing ought to have happened when he heated 'mercury calx' [which we would call mercury oxide], but perhaps the warm August day did not assist clear thought – and the main reason for his experiment seems to be that he was impatient to try out a new piece of equipment on anything that he had to hand. As Priestley himself wrote (in "Experiments and Observations on Different Kinds of Air", 1775): "I cannot, at this distance of time, recollect what it was that I had in view in making this experiment; but I know

I had no expectation of the real issue of it".

"Having procured a lens of twelve inches diameter, I proceeded with great alacrity to examine, by the help of it, what kind of air a great variety of substances, natural and factitious, would yield, putting them into the vessels which I filled with quicksilver and inverted in a basin of the same . . . With this apparatus, after a variety of other experiments, on the first of August, 1774, I endevoured to extract air from mercurius calcinatus per se; and I presently found that by means of this lens, air was expelled from it very readily . . . I admitted water to it and found that it was not imbibed by it. But what surprised me more than I can express was that a candle burned in this air with a remarkably vigorous flame".

LUXURY AIR

In the next few weeks he went on to carry out many experiments with this 'dephlogisticated air', investigating its unusual ability to support combustion, its effect on mice – and on himself. "Being now fully satisfied that this air . . . was much better than common air, and having a quantity of it left . . . I put the mouse into it; when I observed that it seemed to feel no shock upon being put into it . . . but it remained perfectly at its ease another full half hour, when I took it out quite lively and vigorous". When he tried breathing it himself he found it most stimulating and noted: "Who can tell but in time this pure air may become a fashionable article in luxury. Hitherto only two mice and myself have had the pleasure of breathing it."

In the following October he visited Paris and, "knowing that there were several very eminent chemists in that place, I did not omit the opportunity to get an ounce of mercurius calcinatus . . . and I frequently mentioned my surprise at the kind of air which I got from this preparation to Mr Lavoisier, Mr le Roy and several other philosophers."

Although Priestley never fully accepted it, the torch had now passed to Lavoisier (Chapter IV).

PRIESTLEY THE RADICAL

The eighteenth century was not only a time of change and upheaval in science. The Dissenters, from deep religious conviction, were very much concerned with the great questions of liberty and justice. At this time they were still excluded not only from the universities, but from any share in the government. They were sharply critical of the state of the country and pressed for universal suffrage. In Joseph Priestley, together with men such as Richard Price and James Burgh, they had eloquent and powerful advocates for their radical views. Their attitudes made a great impact on the some of rising middle class, but they also made bitter enemies, especially among the establishment and the poor.

Priestley gave his full support to the North American colonists in their struggles with George III and the Prime Minister, Lord North; and he later spoke out in favour of the French Revolution. His views, although strongly radical in these great political issues of the day, also included demands for the abolition of the Poor Laws, which he considered an incitement to idleness. He supported strict controls over the morals of the poor, including the closing down of ale houses, and harsh measures for the suppression and punishment of crime which almost amounted to the reintroduction of slavery.

Boswell's "Life of Johnson" gives us an illustration of the impact Priestley made on his contemporaries, both as a chemist and as a radical:

"Whilst he [Dr Johnson] was in Wiltshire he attended some experiments that were made by a physician at Salisbury on the new kinds of air. In the course of the experiments, frequent mention being made of Dr Priestley, Dr Johnson knit his brows, and in a stern manner inquired, 'Why do we hear so much of Dr Priestley?' He was very properly answered, 'Sir, because we are indebted to him for these important discoveries.'" Boswell commented: "I do not wonder at Johnson's displeasure when the name of Dr Priestley was mentioned; for I know no writer who has been suffered to publish more pernicious doctrines . . . I say nothing of the petulant intemperence with which he dares to insult the venerable establishments of his country."

This great hostility to his views, and especially towards his support for the French Revolution, lead to riots in Birmingham in 1791. The mob set fire to his house and laboratory and for safety he moved to London, where he lived for the next three years.

Eventually he decided to emigrate to America and there Priestley and his family spent the last ten years of his life, cut off from his friends but free to express his political views. He declined the offer of a professorship in chemistry and, in Pennsylvania, he once again set up his own laboratory. There he made one last contribution to 'pneumatic chemistry' by his discovery of carbon monoxide. During these last years he continued to carry on a rearguard action in favour of the phlogiston theory, which had by this time been almost completely abandoned by others. He died in 1804, weakened by the effects of breathing his last "new kind of air", carbon monoxide.

As his legacy to the world Priestley added some vital pieces of information which others would put together to construct the foundations of modern chemistry.

CHAPTER IV

(1743 – 1794)

ANTOINE-LAURENT LAVOISIER

L avoisier was caught up in both of the revolutions which took place in France during the late eighteenth century. His scientific work banished the last remnants of alchemy and laid the foundations of modern chemistry. But despite his great reputation, he became a victim of the other revolution and ended his life on the guillotine.

In many ways Lavoisier's approach to science is in clear contrast to the pragmatism of Joseph Priestley (Chapter III). They both made important contributions to "pneumatic chemistry" (the chemistry of gases), and especially to the understanding of combustion. Unlike Priestley he did not discover any new gases, nor even develop new experimental techniques; his great strength was to refine the work that others had begun; and his precise, methodical approach enabled chemistry to start along the road that physics had taken a century earlier through the work of Isaac Newton.

LAVOISIER THE CIVIL SERVANT

Antoine-Laurent Lavoisier came from a wealthy Parisian family. His original intention was to become a lawyer, but he became fascinated by science and by the time he was twenty he won a prize for outstanding progress. He was elected to the French Academy of Sciences while still only twenty five, and took up a career in what was, in effect, the scientific Civil Service. He was a member of the group which devised the metric system; he helped to draw up the first geological maps of France and was involved in many other practical applications of science, from the introduction of street lighting to increasing the yield of crops. One of his most important official tasks, as a director of state factories, was to make improvements in the manufacture of gunpowder. This was a matter of vital concern for the military strength of France at that time, when supplies could not be imported because of blockades.

THE TAX COLLECTOR

Most of the work for which Lavoisier is now remembered was carried out in his spare time, rather than as part of his official duties. He had inherited the family's estates but in order to buy the equipment for his private experiments he needed to supplement his income; and so he became involved in the collection of taxes. In pre-revolutionary France tax collection was contracted out to a group of aristocrats, who paid a fixed sum for this privilege. Although he suggested reforms in this system (partly out of a sense of justice but perhaps as much on grounds of efficiency), his involvement with this corrupt and unpopular system was later to be one of the main causes of his downfall.

A CHEMICAL REVOLUTION

Lavoisier is associated especially with the development of a new theory of combustion, but he made several other very important contributions which, together, amounted to a revolution in chemistry. He was one of the first to realise the full importance of precise measurements in chemistry and his experiments show a careful, almost fastidious, attention to detail. He devised what amounted to a new language for chemistry and in both his experimental work and in his writing he was determined to impose a new, logical order upon the muddled state of chemistry at that time.

He had valuable assistance from his wife, who became almost a partner in his scientific work. She helped with the publication of his books, drew the illustrations and produced the engravings. She translated scientific publications from England for him, and learned Latin especially for the purpose of translating scientific texts. Some years after her husband's death Mme Lavoisier married another great pioneer of science, Count Rumford.

A NEW THEORY OF COMBUSTION

Lavoisier first became interested in the process of combustion in the early 1770's. He burned phosphorus in a sealed vessel and found that there was no change in weight -until he opened the vessel. When he broke the seal he could hear the air rush in, and he noticed that there was now a small increase in weight. None of this fitted in very convincingly with the existing "phlogiston" theory (Chapter III), but the key to understanding what was really happening was still missing.

Two years later Joseph Priestley visited Paris and met Lavoisier. He described the experiments he had carried out with "calx of mercury" (mercury oxide), and the remarkable new gas he had discovered. In his "Traite Elementaire de Chemie" of 1788 Lavoisier could not quite bring himself to give Priestley full credit for the discovery of oxygen:

"This species of air was discovered almost at the same time by Dr Priestley, Mr Scheele, and myself."

While he overstates his part in the discovery of the new gas, what is beyond question is that Lavoisier was the first to see its real significance. He set about repeating Priestley's experiment, but with typical rigour and far greater attention to detail.

He found that when he heated mercury in a vessel which contained a measured amount of air, the mercury gained weight as it changed to the red "calx of mercury" – and at the same time an equal weight of air disappeared. He went on to separate this calx, weighed it and then heated it more strongly on its own: "When the retort was almost red hot the red matter began gradually to decrease in bulk, and in a few minutes it disappeared altogether; at the same time 41 grains of mercury were collected, and 7 or 8 cubic inches of elastic fluid, greatly more capable of supporting both respiration and combustion than atmospherical air, were collected in the bell-glass."

This "elastic fluid" was Priestley's new gas; and Lavoisier found that the amount he had collected was equal to the amount of air that had disappeared when the original mercury was heated. As the calx turned back to

Lavoisier's apparatus for heating mercury and collecting 'elastic fluid'.

Œuvres de Lavoisier_Tom. III_PL. IX.

A *Grande Lentille à liqueur.*
B *Petite Lentille pour rassembler les raions plus près.*
C *Centre de mouvement horizontal de toute la Machine.*
D *Manivelle servant à imprimer le mouvement horizontal.*
E *Manivelle servant à imprimer le mouvement vertical par le moien des Vis 1 et 2.*
F *Vis de rappel pour éloigner de la grande Loupe la petite Lentille ou la rapprocher.*
G *Porte objet aiant le mouvement de haut en bas et de bas en haut celui d'avancer et reculer parallellement à la plate-forme et de s'incliner au degré du Soleil et de s'avancer parallellement aux raions.*
H *Chariot ou Plate-forme portant toute la Machine et les Opérateurs.*
I *Roues du Chariot tendantes au Centre de mouvement par leurs Axes et roulantes sur des bandes de fer incrustées circulairement sur une plate-forme de pierre.*
K *Escalier pour parvenir sur le Chariot, il est soutenu de deux rouleaux excentriques.*

Lavoisier's design for a huge magnifying glass commissioned by the French Royal Academy of Science, and built by the factory at St. Goblin.

DESSEIN *en Perspective d'une Grande Loupe, formée par 2 Glaces de 52 po. de diam. chacune coulées à la Manufacture Royale de St. Gobin, courbées et travaillées sur une portion de Sphère de 16 pieds de diam. par Mr. de Berniere, Controlleur des Ponts et Chaussées, et ensuite opposées l'une à l'autre par la concavité. L'espace lenticulaire qu'elles laissent entr'elles a été rempli d'esprit de vin il a quatre pieds de diam. et plus de 6 pouc. d'épaisseur au centre: Cette Loupe a été construite d'après le désir de L'ACADÉMIE Roiale des Sciences, aux frais et par les soins de Monsieur DE TRUDAINE, Honoraire de cette Académie, sous les yeux de Messieurs de Montigny, Macquer, Brisson, Cadet et Lavoisier, nommés Commissaires par l'Académie. A Monsieur De Trudaine La Monture a été construite d'après les idées de Mr. de Berniere, perfectionnée et exécutée par Mr. Charpentier, Mécanicien au Vieux Louvre. Par son très humble et très obéissant Serviteur. Charpentier.*

mercury, Lavoisier found that its weight now decreased again – by an amount equal to the weight of gas that had been given off. Everything fitted together.

THE NAMING OF OXYGEN
Lavoisier realised that there were at least two different gases in the air; the active part of the air must be joining up with the material that was burning and this active component was identical to Priestley's gas. His new theory was almost exactly the opposite of the old view. The new theory fitted all the facts – and also gave a much simpler explanation. The phlogiston theory was dead and a new name had to be found for "dephlogisticated air".

Lavoisier came to the conclusion that an acid is formed whenever a substance joins up with this active gas; so he re-named it OXY-GEN, from the Greek words for "acid producer". In fact he was mistaken in this idea that oxygen was the "acid forming principle", but the most important part of his theory was firmly established. Some accepted it at once; for example in 1784 Joseph Black was already explaining it to his students in Edinburgh. Others took longer to make the mental adjustment and a few, like Priestley, continued to cling to the old phlogiston theory until the beginning of the nineteenth century.

A NEW CHEMICAL LANGUAGE
The new name "Oxygen" was part of a general plan to bring order into the confusing terminology that had previously been used in chemistry. Lavoisier considered that the name of a substance should give information about its composition, and he set out to draw up a systematic new language for chemistry, based on his new theory. For example "inflammable air" was re-named hydrogen, which means "water producer" (he had shown that water is in fact hydrogen oxide). His new name for "oil of vitriol" was sulphuric acid; the name tells us that this acid contains sulphur, and the suffix ("-ic") tells us that it contains a certain amount of oxygen. (The name of a related substance, sulphurous acid, tells us that this contains less oxygen and will be a weaker acid). This new terminology was a very important device for spreading Lavoisier's chemical revolution. In 1790,

those who spoke Lavoisier's chemical language, agreed with his new chemistry.

It is difficult now to understand how hard it was for some scientists to accept these new ideas; but Priestley was by no means alone in resisting both the theories and the new terminology based on them, despite the clarity with which Lavoisier presented them. The old names were, however, steadily displaced by Lavoisier's new names, even in everyday speech; and, with some modification, his system is still used in chemistry today.

"LAVOISIER'S PRINCIPLE"

In order to make real progress in understanding the nature of matter, it was necessary to clarify ideas about what is happening when one substance changes into

another. It is quite easy, for example, to imagine that if we burn a piece of paper we are actually destroying the matter from which it is made. Until the eighteenth century, and particularly until the work of Joseph Black and Priestley (Chapter III), gases were largely ignored, and few experimenters had sufficiently accurate apparatus to detect small changes in weight. It was one of Lavoisier's great achievements to establish the importance of meticulous accuracy of measurement, rather than merely subjective observations when carrying out chemical experiments.

From these careful measurements he discovered one of the great principles of science: the Law of Conservation of Matter. His statement of it is a model of clarity:

"We may lay it down as an incontestable axiom, that in all the operations of art and nature, nothing is created; an equal quantity of matter exists both before and after the experiment; the quality and quantity of the elements remain the same; and nothing takes place beyond changes in the combination of these elements."

This has sometimes been called "Lavoisier's Principle" and perhaps it is a pity that this title has not come into general use. Despite his importance to science Lavoisier has never been given the accolade, accorded to many lesser

The death warrant that sent Lavoisier to the guillotine, dated 28th February, 2nd Year of the Republic.

A charming portrait by Jacques Louis David (1748-1825) of Lavoisier and his wife.

men, of having his name commemorated by a scientific law or unit.

THE CHEMICAL ELEMENTS

In his book *Traite Elementaire de Chemie* Lavoisier pursued his objective of bringing greater order to the study of chemistry. It is set out in a systematic way and includes many tables, most notably his list of "Simple Substances". Although their impact was less dramatic than his theory of combustion, this table of the elements, and Lavoisier's comments about them, were an equally important milestone in the construction of modern chemistry.

The most fundamental questions in chemistry is: what are things made of? Since the time of Aristotle the usual answer to this had been that all substances are made up of various mixtures and combinations of the four "elements": earth, air, fire and water. In the sixteenth century the alchemist Paracelsus had put forward an alternative theory of three "principles":

31

mercury, salt and sulphur. By the seventeenth century some combined these two "theories" by adding water and earth to these three, to give a total of five chemical principles.

In "The Sceptical Chymist" (1661), Robert Boyle had attacked the four elements, on the grounds that they were not based on any real evidence. However, at the time when Lavoisier first became interested in chemistry, Aristotle's elements were still firmly established as the basic theory of matter. One of his earliest pieces of work (in 1770), was a series of experiments to disprove the idea that water could be transmuted into earth; but his later work on combustion was to lead to the final demise not only of phlogiston, but also of Aristotle's four elements.

Despite Joseph Priestley's isolation of new "airs", and the work of Henry Cavendish on "inflammable air" (hydrogen), they still regarded these more as varieties of Aristotle's element "air", rather than as distinct materials. It was therefore a very profound change of view when Lavoisier realised that air is in fact composed of two quite separate gases. If air could be taken apart it could no longer be regarded as an element.

When he repeated the experiments of Cavendish on "inflammable air", and reinterpreted the results in terms of his new theory, he not only gave it the new name "hydrogen", but by this name he was indicating that another of Aristotle's elements, water, was really composed of two simpler substances and this too could no longer be regarded as an element.

So, his "Table of Simple Substances" represents a truly revolutionary step in the understanding of chemistry. Lavoisier's own comments on this Table are worth quoting (in the 1790 English translation), and are another example of his clarity of thought:

"The principle object of chemical experiments is to decompose natural bodies, so as separately to examine the different substances which enter into their composition . . . it will be found that this science of chemical analysis has made rapid progress in our own times. Formerly oil and salt were considered as elements of bodies, whereas later observation and experiment have shown that all salts, instead of being simple, are composed of an acid united with a base . . . Thus, as chemistry advances towards perfection, by dividing and subdividing, it is impossible to say where it is to end; and

these things we at present suppose to be simple may soon be found quite otherwise. All we dare venture to affirm of any substance is that it must be considered as simple in the present state of our knowledge, as far as chemical analysis has hitherto been able to show".

This "working definition" of an element – as any substance which cannot be split up into anything simpler by existing techniques, is one of the most important foundation stones of modern chemistry, (and quite fittingly it is the definition still learnt by pupils studying chemistry two hundred years later). After centuries of confusion, Lavoisier had clearly set out the basic programme for answering the ancient question: what things are made of.

It is interesting to note that Lavoisier's table of elements begins with light and "caloric". The latter is the last remnant of Aristotle's element, fire. Francis Bacon (Chapter I) had argued almost two hundred years earlier that heat is related to the motion of atoms, but others, including Lavoisier, continued to maintain that it was a subtle fluid which permeated the pores of ordinary matter. Lavoisier realised that "caloric" had no weight yet, despite having disposed of that other subtle fluid, phlogiston, he regarded heat as a sufficiently real material substance to be included in his table of the elements. This debate was settled in 1798 by Count Rumford (who was later to marry Lavoisier's widow), when he found that an apparently inexhaustible amount of heat was created, by friction, during the boring of cannons; this finally proved that heat could not be a substance but must be a form of energy.

WE DO NOT NEED SAVANTS

In 1794, while he was carrying out an experiment on respiration, Lavoisier was summoned to appear before the Revolutionary Tribunal. He was condemned for his association with the aristocracy, and especially for his involvement in the tax collecting system which had largely paid for his chemical experiments. Despite appeals from his friends, and his great services both to science and to France, the death sentence was passed, and the judge commented: "The Republic has no need of savants".

Within the same month that Priestley was forced to flee to America for his support of the revolution, the guillotine had claimed one of its greatest victims.

CHAPTER V

(1791 – 1867)
MICHAEL FARADAY

It is almost impossible, now, for us to imagine a world without electricity. We almost take it for granted that lighting, communications, transport, cooking and entertainment will all be available at the flick of a switch, and we only realise how much we depend upon electricity on those rare occasions when the power fails and all the services of a town come to a halt.

At the beginning of the last century electricity could only be produced from primitive batteries. It was still a laboratory curiosity, until Faraday made the first dynamo, transformer and electric motor. His discoveries were not applied practically until some years after his death, but his work had pointed the way forward to the large-scale generation of electric power, and all that was later to come from this. In a very real sense Michael Faraday helped to make the world as we know it today. This is his most obvious achievement, but he made very important contributions to many other areas of physics

and chemistry and his lesser achievements tend to be overshadowed: for example, he was the first person to liquefy chlorine and to make a detailed investigation of several chemicals, such as benzene. His stature, as one of the world's greatest scientists, and perhaps the greatest scientific educator of the nineteenth century, is all the more remarkable if we consider his origins.

A SELF-MADE MAN
James Faraday, his father, was a blacksmith in the tiny hamlet of Outhgill in a remote valley in Westmorland, and Margaret, his mother, was a servant at a nearby farm in Deepgill. They were deeply religious people, members of a very strict sect known as the Sandemans who met for worship in the nearest town, Kirkby Stephen. In 1791 they set out for London and there Michael, their third child was born in the September of the same year. The family did not find that London was paved with gold, and they were unable to afford anything more than a

very elementary education for the young boy. So at the age of thirteen he started work with a bookseller, first as a messenger boy and later as an apprentice bookbinder.

This proved to be a fortunate choice of trade. His employer allowed him to read many of the books that were sent in for binding and he soon became an avid reader, making detailed notes about the books which most interested him. By the age of nineteen he had developed a keen interest in science and was already carrying out his own simple experiments, limited by the few pence he could spare to buy equipment. In 1812 he came to the attention of one of the customers, Mr Dance, a member of the Royal Institution, who gave Faraday tickets to attend four lectures by Sir Humphrey Davy. These lectures fired Faraday's enthusiasm; he took detailed notes and made illustrations of the experiments, then later bound all these into a book.

THE ROYAL INSTITUTION

By this time his apprenticeship was coming to an end. He wrote to Sir Humphrey Davy to ask whether there was any possibility of becoming an assistant in the laboratories of the Royal Institution, and he also enclosed the book he had produced from his lecture notes. Davy replied that there were no vacancies in the laboratory, but recommended that he should keep to his trade as a bookbinder; he promised that would use his services to bind some of the publications of the Royal Institution. Then by a stroke of good fortune, an assistant was dismissed a few weeks later. Davy remembered Faraday's request and he engaged him, by now aged twenty two, to take his place. He immediately proved his worth, showing a natural aptitude for making apparatus and assisting with experiments. Within two years he received his first public recognition, when Sir Humphrey Davy recorded that he was "indebted to Mr Faraday for much able assistance" in his work on the construction of the "Davy lamp" for miners.

By now Michael Faraday's career as a scientist was fully launched, and in the following year he gave his first lecture and published the first of his many papers. In 1820 he married a fellow member of the Sandeman sect

Faraday lecturing before an audience including the Prince Consort and The Prince of Wales at the Royal Institution.

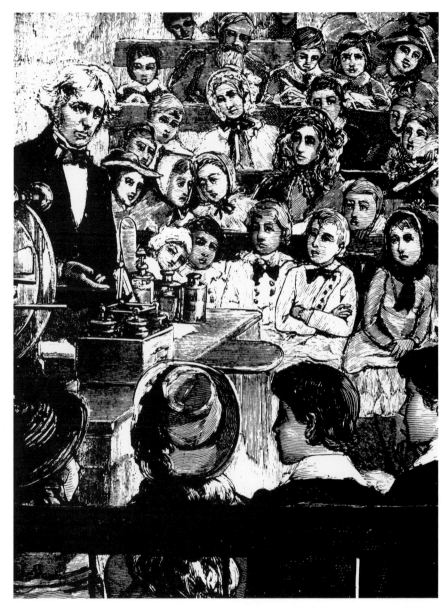

Faraday demonstrating electricity to children at his Christmas lecture in 1846.

and the couple took up residence in the Royal Institution building in Albermarle Street. His rapid progress continued; by 1823 he was elected a Fellow of the Royal Society and in the following year he became the Director of the Royal Institution laboratory.

The Royal Institution was at that time still quite a recent foundation. In the 1790's the Anglo-American scientist Benjamin Thompson, (who had been awarded the title of Count Rumford for his services to the Bavarian army – see also chapter IV), returned to London and drew up a proposal for the setting up of "a Public Institution for diffusing the knowledge and facilitating the general introduction of useful mechanical inventions". This received a good response; the Institution was set up in 1799 and received its royal charter in January 1800. The new body soon began to

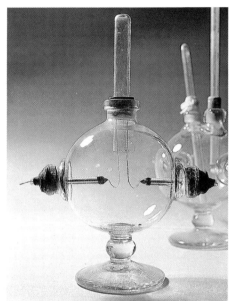

Faraday's electrolysis apparatus of 1834, by which he measured the electrochemical effects of differing electrical sources.

A contemporary drawing of Michael Faraday in his laboratory at the Royal Institution in Albermarle St.

fulfil Rumford's hopes, and in 1801 the newly appointed Director of the Laboratory, Humphrey Davy, gave the first of his public lectures. These soon became so popular and fashionable that Albermarle Street became blocked by carriages at the time of the lectures and was made a one-way street. The Royal Institution was not only a success as an educational body but was soon producing important scientific work. It was there that Davy first produced sodium and potassium by the new process of electrolysis. Together with Faraday, Davy established a great international reputation for the Institution and this has been maintained by other notable Directors, including Sir George Porter (who was awarded a Nobel Prize in chemistry in 1967 for the work he carried out there).

FARADAY'S LAWS

Faraday continued the work that Davy had begun, passing electricity through chemicals to investigate how they are affected by it. He also invented words to describe what is going on during this process, which he named electrolysis. He introduced the new word "ion", to describe an electrically charged atom, the terms "electrode", "anode" and "cathode" for the positive and negative electrodes, and "electrolyte" for those substances which can be broken up by electricity.

He discovered that there are important relationships between the amount of electricity passed through a substance and the amount of new substances that are set free – these became known as Faraday's Laws. They were an important (and useful) discovery in themselves, but Faraday's Laws also had a deeper significance by showing that atoms are associated only with definite amounts of electricity. This was not fully explained until the early years of this century, when Rutherford and others worked out the structure of atoms. Faraday's discoveries in the field of electrochemistry were published in three volumes, between 1839 and 1855, under the title "Experimental Researches in Electricity". Together they are a contribution to the borderline between physics and chemistry important enough to ensure that Faraday would have a significant place in the history of science, even if he had not made what proved to be even greater discoveries in electromagnetism.

ELECTRICITY AND MAGNETISM

Since at least the eighteenth century there had been a marked difference in approach to science on the two sides of the channel. The empirical approach of Priestley, in contrast to the systematic methods of Lavoisier (Chapters III and IV), is a typical example. Faraday, in many respects, shared this British leaning towards pragmatism. It was perhaps further accentuated by his lack of formal education, and especially by his very limited knowledge of mathematics. What would have been a severe limitation for a lesser man proved to be a spur to the genius of Michael Faraday.

In the early years of the nineteenth century the nature of electricity was still one of the greatest mysteries and one of the most hotly debated topics in science. Benjamin Franklin, in the previous century, had put forward the theory that it was a fluid; some considered positive and negative electricity to be two different fluids; but Faraday saw it rather as a force. Magnetism also excited much interest, but no direct link had yet been discovered between these two forces.

It was therefore of great interest to scientists when a connection between magnetism and electricity was discovered in 1820. The Danish scientist Hans Oersted found that a wire carrying an electric current caused the movement of a compass needle. Many other experiments were carried out throughout Europe where Ampère, by a combination of his experimental work and mathematical ability, built up a theory of the magnetic effects of an electric current.

But one of the most important breakthroughs came

because Faraday had an intuitive feeling that there should be a matching opposite effect. He felt sure that the magnetic effect produced in one coil of wire "ought to" cause (or induce) an electric current to be set up in a second coil. In 1831 he began many experiments using an iron ring which had two coils of wire wound around it. One of the coils was connected to a battery, the other went to a sensitive meter (a galvanometer), for detecting if any current was produced. But Faraday failed to find the effect he had expected, even when he passed large electric currents through the coil. Then on one occasion he noticed that that the galvanometer gave a small movement – not while the current was flowing through the coil, but at the moment it was switched off or on.

His intuition had proved to be right, after all, and he followed this with many other experiments, including a demonstration that a moving magnet alone could induce an electric current. He had discovered the principle of the dynamo, and from this work others would soon go on

Faraday's disk dynamo experiment of 1831, in which a moving magnet produces an electrical current.

The original Magnetic Spark apparatus of 1831. A spark was produced when the handles pulled the coiled wire sharply away from the magnet.

to develop many practical applications, including the large scale production of electricity, and inventions such as the telephone (chapter XV). Like others he was aware of the importance of this work, although even he could not have realised just how important it would later prove to be. There is, though, a story that Sir Robert Peel, the Prime Minister, asked him what use the dynamo would be. Faraday is said to have answered: "I don't know, but I'll wager that one day your government will tax it".

IN HIS MIND'S EYE

Rather than develop any of the practical applications, Faraday himself was more concerned with exploring new ideas about magnetism and electricity. Here again his intuition perhaps helped rather than hindered by his lack of mathematics, was to achieve striking results. In trying to understand how a magnet can affect a wire some distance away from it, Faraday visualised that the space itself around the magnet was under strain. This "magnetic field" he visualised as consisting of lines of magnetic force, closer together where the field was stronger; and an electric current was produced when a wire cut through these lines of force. He carried out a vivid experiment, which many have since seen repeated in school science lessons. As Sir George Porter says: "I recommend anyone who hasn't seen it to do it, because it's great fun. You get a magnet and put a piece of paper over it, then sprinkle iron filings. Pins will do, but iron filings are best. Then if you tap it, the iron filings make beautiful patterns joining the north to the south poles of the magnet. They actually draw out for you the lines of force, and they make it very real. Faraday liked to see things which looked very real."

This way of visualising the effects of a magnet, as a "field" stretching out all around it, but getting weaker the further away you get from it, at first received little support from other scientists, who expected theories to be expressed in a mathematical form. But to Faraday's intuitive mind, it raised many further questions. For example, one of the unorthodox conclusions that he drew was that a magnet should have an effect on light. He imagined that the whole of space was filled with these lines of force, and that perhaps light consisted of vibrations travelling along them. Faraday carried out many experiments before he was eventually able to show that light could, in fact, be influenced – polarised light can be rotated by a magnetic field. It took more than twenty years for orthodox physics to catch up with this intuition, and James Clerk Maxwell was eventually able to produce a mathemetical theory which completed the synthesis of magnetism with electricity, and their link with light (chapter VI).

THE GREAT SCIENTIFIC COMMUNICATOR

Faraday, perhaps remembering his own struggle to gain knowledge, was an enthusiastic populariser of science in Victorian England. He continued Davy's tradition of giving lectures on science for general audiences at the Royal Institution, and in 1826 he started the Friday evening lectures, which still continue today. They attracted a wide and fashionable audience, and Prince Albert started to bring the royal children to some of them. Faraday believed that the enthusiasm for science should begin as early as possible and he started another new series, the Christmas lectures, illustrated by some spectacular experiments. These, too, are still an annual event and are now extended to an even wider audience by television. One of his own most famous Christmas lectures, which he repeated several times, was later published as a book for children: "The Chemical History of a Candle".

THE LAST YEARS OF "PLAIN MICHAEL FARADAY"

At intervals over the years Faraday had suffered from the great work-load that he imposed upon himself, and sometimes his health required that he stop work entirely and go for a long holiday. Apart from these breaks, he continued to work and live at the Royal Institution until 1858, taking long weekends by the sea. In this year, when he was now sixty seven, the Queen awarded him a "house of grace and favour" at Hampton Court palace, at the suggestion of Prince Albert. He continued to live there for his last nine years, often travelling up to the Royal Institution for the Friday lectures and also for the Christmas lectures, which he last gave in 1860.

Throughout his life he had tried to live up to the religious faith that had been passed on to him by his parents, and he never lost sight of his humble origins. In these last years he was recognised as one of the great men of his time; many honours were offered, but few were accepted. He said that the only honour that he had ever wanted was his Fellowship of the Royal Society. He declined the chair of chemistry at London University, and on being offered, and refusing, the Presidency of the Royal Society he replied: "I must remain plain Michael Faraday to the last". In his biography of 1869, John Tyndall wrote: "He had not a trace of worldly ambition; he declared his duty to his sovereign by going to the levee once a year, but beyond this he never sought contact with the great".

He continued to work, write and give lectures from time to time, up to 1865. His last investigation was to be an attempt to discover whether a magnetic field takes time to be propagated. He constructed some of the apparatus, but after a struggle he realised that the effort was now too great for him and he gave up the project. (Perhaps this was one last great intuitive leap; the answer to this important question would have to wait for James Clerk Maxwell (see chapter VI), who would develop Faraday's ideas further.

Shortly after this his health deteriorated further and for a time he lost his memory entirely, possibly due to mercury poisoning from his work in the laboratory over the years. He spent his last two years, as he put it, "in waiting"; and on 25th August, 1867, at the age of 76, he died in his sleep, sitting in a chair in his study at Hampton Court.

CHAPTER VI

(1831 - 1879)
JAMES CLERK MAXWELL

While the great names of Newton and Einstein are familiar even to non-scientists around the world, it will usually be a physicist whose eyes light up at the mention of James Clerk Maxwell. Although he didn't build engines, bridges, or make any of those magnificent technological contributions which dominate our perspective of scientific progress, this modest, unflamboyant Scot is now held to be the greatest theoretical physicist of the nineteenth century. It was Maxwell's intuitive mathematics which enabled the transition from Newton's Frame of Nature to Einstein's revolutionary leap in the understanding of our universe.

Maxwell's name is linked to many theories and inventions, showing the vast range of subjects to which he applied his genius. Not only did he revolutionize the nineteenth-century concepts of electricity, magnetism and light, taking the first colour photograph and predicting the existence of radio waves years before anyone else, he was also an astronomer, an engineer, a poet and something of a mystic. According to John Maddox of *Nature* magazine, he was able to make intuitive links that were beyond his contemporaries in science:

"It must be said, because I think it's true, that apart from being a quite outstanding mathematician, Maxwell did have a physical intuition, a feeling for physical concepts that's quite unique . . . unlike many of his contemporaries who were also distinguished mathematicians, he was able to admit concepts that other people rejected simply because they seemed strange. And that is why he was able, by pure thought, to make such quite remarkable progress."

'DAFTIE MAXWELL' OF GLENLAIR

Maxwell had always had this intellectual independence. He was an only child born to doting middle-aged parents, on the estate of Glenlair in Galloway in 1831. As his proud mother described in a letter to her sister, even as a two year old his curiosity was endless:

"He is a very happy man, and . . . has great work with doors, locks, keys, etc., and 'show me how it does' is never out of his mouth. He also investigates the hidden course of streams and bell wires, the way the water gets from the pond through the wall and down a drain into Water Orr, then past the smiddy and down to the sea . . . "

His mother died of cancer when Maxwell was seven, after an agonising and futile operation to try and save her life. These were the days before anaesthetics. Maxwell was brought up by his father, a kindly, conscientious and eccentric man who insisted on designing every object he used, from his house to his clothes. When the eight-year old Maxwell was delivered to his first school, the Edinburgh Academy, he presented a woeful sight to the sniggering schoolboys. His father had designed his grey tweed tunic and square-toed boots with bronze clasps, while his aunt had added a frilly collar. It was years before he became grudgingly respected for his pleasant, uncompromising nature: to most of the boys he was "daftie Maxwell", always small for his age, who stuttered in a Galloway brogue and spent his spare time collecting scrap, wires and beetles to use in his experiments.

LIGHT, OVALS AND STARS
Edinburgh was a fertile intellectual environment, however lonely it might have been otherwise. Maxwell spent parts of his holidays with the extraordinarily gifted sons of William Thompson, then Professor of Mathematics at Glasgow, and was regularly shepherded by his father to meetings of the Royal Society of Edinburgh. His scientific inquiries progressed by leaps and bounds. When he was fourteen he published his first paper in the April 1846 issue of the Royal Society of Edinburgh, on his discovery of a new way to draw the perfect oval. Maxwell was also introduced to the Edinburgh Observatory where he could track the planets and stars, .which laid the foundations of his later researches into the mysterious rings of Saturn.

The behaviour of light increasingly came to fascinate him, especially the way crystals can split, or polarize, light into two refracted parts. Although by the first half of the nineteenth century it was already understood that light travels in waves, here was a phenomenon that demonstrated how light travelled in transverse waves. It was still beyond the limits of science to explain why this

should be so, and again Maxwell was to investigate and fully explain the nature of light waves in the years to come. The great Edinburgh physicist James Nichol gave public lectures at which he demonstrated the polarisation of light in any desired direction through crystals made of Iceland Spar. The professor was so impressed by the avid young Maxwell that he gave him a pair of these crystals, which he treasured all his life.

In 1850 Maxwell went to study mathematics at Trinity College, Cambridge. This was after much soul-searching by his Calvinist father, who was afraid that his brilliant son might become tainted by the various lush varieties of Anglicanism flourishing at the time. He need not have worried: his son never altered the deep religious convictions he had inherited, and an eccentric study regime left him little time for theological hair-splitting. A contemporary student complained of his habit of exercising around the college at 2 o'clock in the morning "by running along the upper corridor, down the stairs, then up the stairs, and so on, until the inhabitants of the rooms along his track got up to have shots at him with boots, hairbrushes, etc., as he passed."

Nevertheless his genius was transparently obvious to them, even if it was once manifested, as a fellow undergraduate teasingly reminded him years later, by his inventing a new method of throwing cats out of windows so that they couldn't land on their feet. It was a charge which Professor Maxwell later staidly denied.

THE ELECTRIC CENTURY
During Maxwell's youth, a scientific revolution had been unleashed. Faraday was still completing his researches into electromagnetism, which were to become the foundations for Maxwell's own work. England was the world hub of developing mechanisation, and had made great scientific strides forward: the simply formulated laws of thermodynamics, for example, which set down the physics of heat and the nature of its energy, would alter man's thinking about the whole nature of the universe. However, the link between the phenomena of electricity, magnetism and the nature of light had not yet been perceived; they were still regarded as separate fields of enquiry. By the end of the 1850's, when Maxwell was Professor of Natural Philosophy at Aberdeen, he began to prove a series of scientific connections which would lay the foundations of modern physics.

The planet Saturn with its mysterious rings, which Maxwell proved were made up of dense particles.

GASES AND THE RINGS OF SATURN

In 1859, after years of pondering the nature of the rings around the planet Saturn, Maxwell published a monumental monograph *On the nature of Saturn's Rings* in which he proved that the rings were not solid, but were made up of many small particles that flew around in a dense confusion which he compared to the shot-filled air of the recent Siege of Sebastopol. Maxwell demonstrated that the paths of these particles were not, in fact, as random as they appeared, and when measured the oscillations of the particles fell into wave patterns. It was an astonishing deduction, and won Maxwell the Adams Prize for mathematics.

His thinking about the Rings of Saturn led Maxwell to publish a second landmark paper in the same year, *The Dynamical Theory of Gases*. While his new wife Katherine stoked the boilers in the basement of their home to maintain a constant temperature in Maxwell's attic laboratory, he mathematically proved the earlier, and rather overlooked, view of Bernouilli and Herapath that a gas consisted of innumerable minute particles flying about and colliding in all directions. If the molecules were of the same temperature, there was no transferred energy when they collided, but if one was hotter than the other, the faster-moving hot molecules

O.T! R.U. ATOME? $\iint S\, \text{phase}^2\, dS$ was done in the most general form in 1867. I have now bagged ξ & η from T & T' and done the numerical value of $\iint (Y_i^{(s)})^2 dS$ in 4 lines, thus verifying $T + T'$'s value of $\iint (Q_i^{(s)})^2 dS$. Your plan seems indept of $T + T'$ or of me. Publish! I am busy supplying the physical necessities of scientific life. Address 11 Scroope Terrace, Cambridge. Prooves have got as far as grooves, corrugated plates, gratings and rings. If you have time for criticism they shall be sent.

$$\iint (Y_i^{(s)})^2 dS = \frac{8\pi a^2}{2i+1} \frac{\underline{i+s}}{2^{2s}} \frac{\underline{i-s}}{\underline{i}\,\underline{i}}$$

except when $S = 0$ when $\iint (Q_i)^2 dS = \frac{4\pi a^2}{2i+1}$

Hence $\displaystyle\int_{-1}^{+1} (Q_i^{(s)})^2 d\mu = \frac{2}{2i+1} \frac{2^{2s}\,\underline{i-s}\,\underline{\underline{s}}\,\underline{\underline{s}}}{\underline{i+s}}$ without exception

$\text{yrs } \frac{d}{dt}$

A postcard from Maxwell to his
colleague at the Cavendish
laboratory, P. G. Tait.

would transfer their heat to the cooler ones. Despite these transfers of energy, the total amount of energy generated in the universe remained constant, just like some vast stock exchange where millions of 'energy' units could be gained or lost by being converted into different 'currencies' of heat, electricity, light, and so on.

Scientists were now able to imagine clearly how the universe was made up of corporal atoms and molecules, motivated by incorporal agencies: heat, light, magnetism and electricity. Most scientists of the nineteenth century still believed that the forces involved could not operate through empty space, but needed some sort of medium to carry them, which they could only describe as 'the ether'. Although for the purposes of his explanations, Maxwell also needed to refer to the ether, he privately doubted its existence, and his equations certainly worked with or without it.

THE FIRST COLOUR PHOTOGRAPH

While Maxwell pondered the nature of gases, he was also investigating colour, spending many hours bent over his 'colour box' – a long wooden box into which the sun shone: his appalled neighbours thought it was a coffin. In 1860 he presented his *Theory of Colour Vision,* in which he established the fundamental properties of the primary colours: red, green and blue, working out what proportions needed to be mixed with each other to produce all the other colours. The following year he displayed the first ever colour photograph, of his wife's tartan ribbon. This was achieved by an untypical mixture of good luck as well as brilliance: the idea was to take a black and white photograph through three separate filters, blue, red and green, then project the superimposed negatives through the same filters and photograph the result. Although the early photographic process was not supposed to be sensitive to red, it turned out instead to be sensitive to the ultraviolet light passed by the filter, giving the same desired result.

MAXWELL'S GREAT CONNECTION

Maxwell's next, and most spectacular move, was to work out the link between light, electricity and magnetism. Newton (see chapter II) had proved his law of gravity as a funadmental law of what was viewed as a 'mechanistic' universe, in which masses of different sizes, like electrical charges, were simply attracted to each other. The great scientist Faraday (see chapter V) had already observed that these charges created a 'disturbance' around them, rather than just upon each other, and found it more accurate to talk of an electro-magnetic 'force field' which is created by a single charge of electricity. This field exists in space (or, as was believed in the nineteenth century, in the ether), whether another charge comes in to be affected by the force field or not. It has its own reality, independent of any physical bodies.

In 1873 Maxwell proved and refined this subtle and revolutionary idea of Faraday's through four simple equations, in his famous *Treatise on Electricity and Magnestism.* It perfectly summed up Maxwell's life's work, by combining the laws of electricity and magnetism into one set of mathematical equations. Even more startling, and beautifully clear, was Maxwell's inspired culmination to the treatise.

The question of the exact nature of light had puzzled scientists since Newton, and Maxwell since his experiments with crystals in Edinburgh. By adding an extra mathematical term he found he could make the laws of electricity and magnetism perfectly compatible, and allowed scientists to discover solutions to equations which described waves travelling for ever throughout space. Each wave produced a varying magnetic field, which in turn produced a varying electric field. The solution to the equation produced a constant which was equal to the velocity of light.

The connection was simple: light itself was nothing more than a rapidly vibrating electromagnetic field, travelling in waves through space. As light is made up of different colours, each of which travels at different frequencies of vibrations, he predicted that light must only be one phenomenon somewhere in the scale of electromagnetic vibrations. What happened when the electromagnetic field vibrated more slowly? Or more quickly? He was sure that there must be other forms of electro-magnetic radiation, and sure enough, after Maxwell's death, Hertz proved him right through the sensational discovery of the lower frequency radio waves in 1888. In 1896, Röntgen (chapter XIX) demonstrated Maxwell's prediction by the discovery of X-Rays towards the other end of the electromagnetic spectrum. Today we know that the sequence of waves in the spectrum goes from radio waves to microwaves, then infra-red, light, ultra-violet, X-rays, then gamma rays, vibrating at almost unimaginably high frequencies so that they can penetrate lead walls two feet thick.

MAXWELL'S LEGACY

In 1873 Maxwell died of cancer at the tragically early age of forty-eight. Outside the world of physics he was still unknown, although he had become the first director of the Cavendish scientific laboratory in Cambridge, then probably the world centre of physics research. In addition to his research, he gave up some of his time to teach physics in evening classes to working men, but unfortunately his lectures were not a success. Maxwell still had not got over his stutter and soft-spoken shyness. Also, his thoughts raced ahead of his explanations so quickly that he could only give his hapless listeners scattered clues, making his lectures almost incomprehensible. Despite his good intentions, he could not help his impatience with the intellectual laggards in the audience. Nevertheless he retained a mischievous sense of humour, and never lost the habit of firing off jaunty satirical verses on any aspect of current scientific politics that amused him.

Maxwell had been so far-sighted that it took a while for contemporary physicists to catch up, some opposing his radical changes to the rules of science up to the turn of the century. It was not really until 1916, and Einstein's *Theory of Relativity* (see chapter XXIV), that Maxwell's work was fully appreciated. Einstein had used Maxwell's field equations as the basis for his great Theory, which transformed physics into the nuclear age: a step that could not have been taken but for Maxwell's quiet brilliance.

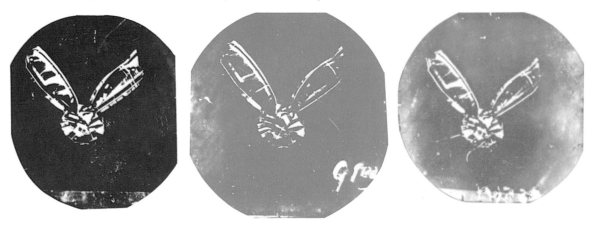

The tartan ribbon belonging to Maxwell's wife, photographed through three colour filters and superimposed to produce the first colour photograph.

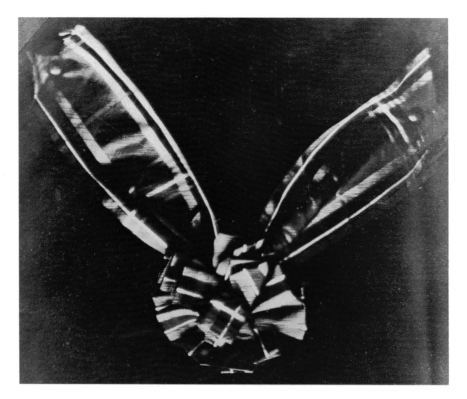

CHAPTER VII

(1797 – 1875)
SIR CHARLES LYELL

"In the beginning, God created heaven, and earth . . . God said: Let the waters that are under the heaven, be gathered together in one place, and let the dry land appear. And it was so done.

And God called the dry land Earth, and the gathering together of the waters, he called Seas. And God saw that it was good."

For centuries, Western civilization had taken for granted the Biblical account of the creation. Serious calculations to discover the age of the world were made based on the generations mentioned in the Bible, and the answer seemed to be exactly 4004 years, according to one Bishop Ussher. Beyond the collection of rock and fossils for their curiosity value, nobody thought to take geology, the study of the earth, very seriously.

"NO VESTIGE OF A BEGINNING, NO PROSPECT OF AN END"

The status of this obscure science was changed in 1788 when an Edinburgh physician, James Hutton, published a remarkable thesis entitled *Theory of the Earth*. In it, Hutton put forward a beautifully simple and obvious theory for the development of the landscape that no-one had thought of before: the rock forms, mountains, valleys and shorelines were formed by the same natural processes that are visible to us today: glaciers, wind and frost erosion, wave action and volcanoes. Hand in hand with these ideas came the suggestion that the world must be very much older than had previously been thought. But Hutton's most revolutionary concept was that the world was continually reforming itself in endless cycles:

mountains were thrown up, became eroded over millions of years, then were created again. Seas rose and fell, valleys were created and gradually diminished, rivers flowed, altered their courses, dried up, then sprang anew elsewhere. In this geological process Hutton declared he could find "no vestige of a beginning, no prospect of an end."

Many geologists (quite apart from the general public) were unwilling to accept such a shocking idea which flew in the face of every familiar assumption about the creation of the world. They found it preposterous to suggest, as some Huttonites did, that the world was possibly five hundred million years old. Today we think the age of the earth is nearer five thousand million years!

The man who was largely responsible for spreading the new ideas in geology was Sir Charles Lyell. In a clearly and elegantly written book, *The Principles of Geology* written in 1830-3, Lyell put the case for a scientific aproach to geology before the public. He was not so much concerned with the minutiae of classification of fossils, strata, or making maps, what interested Lyell was the broad sweep of what geology was all about. He insisted on the vital importance of field work and travel, which many until then had considered to be nothing but the jaunts of harmless fanatics. To observe closely how the landscape had changed and continued to do so, and draw conclusions, was the life-blood of geology. Lyell's book was a tremendous success and had far-reaching reprecussions: among the many scientists and naturalists it inspired was the young Charles Darwin setting off on his epic voyage in *The Beagle*.

THE GENTLEMAN GEOLOGIST

In the early nineteenth century, geologists and naturalists were mainly found among the affluent middle classes, with endless time to spend and no real career in mind. Geology was considered a hobby, it certainly had no real scientific status despite the learned dissertations on the subject read out at scientific societies in France, Germany and Britain.

Charles Lyell was no exeception to this pattern. He was born into a wealthy Scottish family 1797, which travelled widely and at a leisurely pace in Britain and on the continent during Lyell's youth. His education was consequently a fairly casual undertaking, punctuated by illness. Long after his family considered it appropriate for

boys to indulge in such pastimes, Charles secretly continued to hunt birdsnests, butterflies, and keep accurate seasonal charts of the life cycles of many insects. To the disgust of the servants he kept an aquarium of newts and frog-spawn under his bed, but found an ally in his father's footman, with whom he would sort beetles and watch birds to his heart's content.

WILLIAM BUCKLAND

By the time Charles went to Oxford in 1816, geology had already become an additional interest. He had the good fortune to attend the lectures of William Buckland, the most charismatic and enthusiastic geologist of the time. Every student wanted to show their geological samples to him, with the result that his lodgings were heaped with fossil fragments, rocks and trilobites flowing over the breakfast table and onto the floor. After one particularly successful dinner party he told his guests they had been eating fifty thousand year old mammoth steaks, freshly dug out of the Siberian ice: no-one could be absolutely sure that he was joking. Through studying with this extraordinary man, Lyell became especially interested in the geological features of Britain, in particular the striking basalt formations of Fingal's cave off the Isle of Mull in Scotland, which was caused by the rapid cooling of lava.

THE FORCES OF NATURE

Geology had become genteel enough to interest the whole of Lyell's family, and he joined them on a trip throughout France and Switzerland to study the action of glaciers. The destruction they wreaked was awesome, inundating villages in mud slides or crushing down" the tallest pines with as much ease as an elephant would the herbage of a meadow." He also saw for himself how large rocks were carried along in the mud stream tributaries of glaciers, and noted vast slabs of granite rock above his path. He could not account for their existence then; later he would realise that they had been carried along by the glaciers of the Ice Age and left as the glaciers had gradually melted. The impressions Lyell was accumulating were soon to convince him of the soundness of Hutton's ideas, still not widely known or accepted over twenty years later.

When Lyell left Oxford he was obliged to make a more serious attempt at finding a career. Law seemed

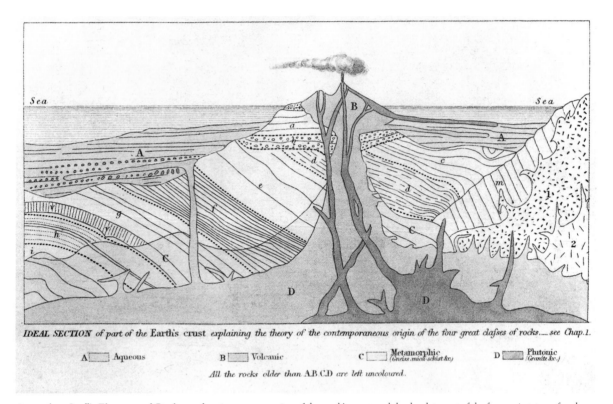

IDEAL SECTION *of part of the Earth's crust explaining the theory of the contemporaneous origin of the four great classes of rocks.* __ see Chap.1.

A [ ] Aqueous   B [ ] Volcanic   C [ ] Metamorphic *(Gneiss.mica-schist &c.)*   D [ ] Plutonic *(Granite &c.)*

All the rocks older than A.B.C.D are left uncoloured.

A page from Lyell's Elements of Geology, *showing a cross-section of the earth's crust and the development of the four main types of rock which he identified: (A) Aqueous (sedimentary), (B) Volcanic, (C) Metamorphic, (D) Plutonic (formed deep in the earth's crust – the regions of Pluto, God of the Underworld).*

respectable enough for a man of his station, and rather unwillingly he tried to buckle down. However, his eyes became over-strained, and while he recuperated, Charles struck up an influential friendship with a Sussex geologist, Gideon Mantell. They talked about fossils through the night into morning on their first meeting and carried on a lively exchange of letters. The study of law retreated further into the background: from now on, geology was to dominate Lyell's life.

THE GEOLOGICAL TIME SCALE

By 1827 Lyell was in Sicily, examining the fossils of sea-shells which were imbedded in sedimentary rocks (made up over thousands of years from sand and mud compressed into rock) which alternated with lava rocks. These shells had been found at a height of almost four thousand feet up the volcanic mountain of Etna, and

provided strong evidence that there had been tremendous land upheavals in Sicily. The idea was forming in Lyell's mind that if such structures as the volcano Mount Etna was a relatively recent one, in geological terms, the world must still be in a process of being structurally shaped. Land was rising and falling all the time, coastines were being eroded and added to, glaciers were creeping forward, carrying rocks and gouging valleys behind them.

He also realised that the way geological time was measured in the early nineteenth century was not accurate enough. He had discovered shells from what was known as the most recent *Tertiary* era (up to sixty five million years), but of vastly varying ages. These ages could be calculated by observing what quantity of shells were found in the various rock strata: the older the rock, the fewer shells there would be. In this way, the Tertiary

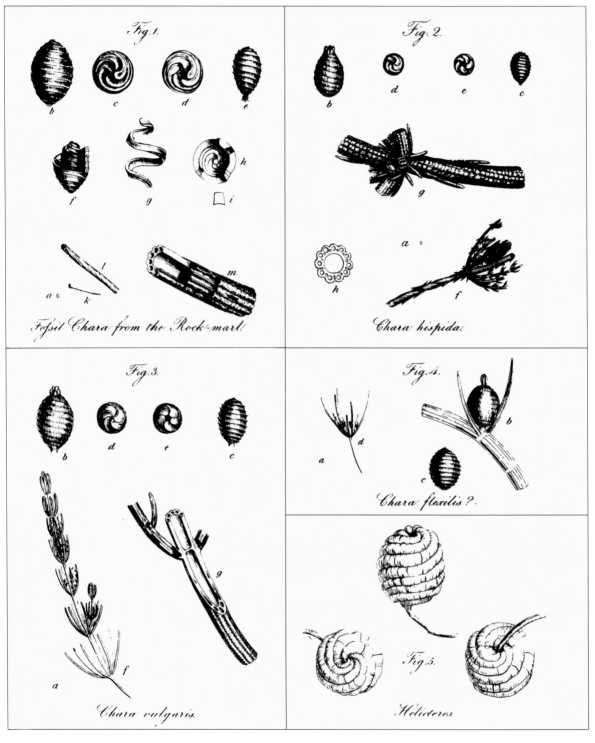

Fig.1.

Fofsil Chara from the Rock-marl.

Fig.2.

Chara hispida.

Fig.3.

Chara vulgaris.

Fig.4.

Chara flexilis?.

Fig.5.

Helicteres.

era could be quite precisely divided up into the seven periods that geologists use today.

GEOLOGICAL BATTLE LINES

Like every other academic discipline that has ever existed, the young science of geology was no stranger to opposing factions. Nineteenth century geology was perhaps a particularly sensitive area, overlapping into religion and philosophy. No-one knew for certain how old the earth was, or how it had come into existence. Plenty of people held strong views on the matter. At the time, they were roughly divided into two camps, the *Catastrophists* and the *Uniformitarians*.

The Catastrophists believed in an essentially Christian universe which was created according to a pre-ordained plan, and subject to supernatural intervention. The geology of the planet had been created long ago by a series of worldwide cataclysmic disturbances, which destroyed all, or almost all, existing life. These crises were interspersed with long periods of calm when life was created anew, each species separately, rather than evolving out of the other. The theory accounted for breaks in the fossil record, with each fossil being regarded as a prophecy of the ultimate aim of creation: man. Although Catastrophism allowed for the intervention of inexplicable natural and supernatural forces, this was not always directly acknowledged. Analagous to the Catastrophists were the Progressionists, who believed that life had developed from simple to more complex forms, succeeding each other through the eras of the past, but not necessarily genetically descending from each other. Along with the Catastrophists, they believed man to be the summit and purpose of all creation.

The Uniformitarians, on the other hand, believed only in the natural forces that they could see at work in the world around them. they rejected the idea of a world created according to a design and time-scale; for the uniformitarian the world was still developing and changing, slowly but ceaselessly. The timeless questions

Lyell's drawing of the various fossil shells found in the chalk marl, by means of which he was able to date the rock strata.

of why the earth existed and what its purpose was were beyond human understanding, they decided, and therefore they were wary of accepting any view of creation continuing in an upward trend.

Problems such as the origins of life, the appearance of new fossil forms in the rocks and the fact that fossils *did* record a chronological trend towards greater sophistication, from early sea creatures to the mammal remains of the Tertiary era, were consequently easier for the catastrophists to explain. In an increasingly scientific climate however, these explanations became less satisfactory. The extreme forms of both views began to falter. What was to tip the argument firmly and, (with modifications) permanently onto the side of the uniformitarians, was Charles Lyell's publication of the first volume of *Principles of Geology* in 1830.

"FREEING SCIENCE FROM MOSES"

The first volume of Lyell's great work pulled together the latest in British, German and French uniformitarian thinking. In a letter to his friend George Scrope, secretary of the Geological Society, Lyell declared that his principle aim was to "free science from Moses" – in other words, to put forward an account of the formation of the earth that was not constrained to conform with the Bible's version.

Lyell's approach was self-explanatory in the full title: *Principles of Geology: being an attempt to explain the former changes of the earth's surface by reference to causes now in operation.*

In the first chapter, Lyell states firmly that geology must be separated from cosmology to make any sense at all. He entertainingly described how the ancient traditions of India, Egypt and Greece first accounted for the creation of the world, with their emphases on alternating periods of creation and destruction. These traditions probably arose in response to catastrophes such as floods and volcanoes which could destroy local settlements and communities instantly. Lyell journeys through history, listing the many instances when geological speculation was hampered, first by the emergence of Islam in the 7th century AD, and then by the European Christian reliance on biblical history.

In 1751 the Faculty of Theology in Paris forced the geologist Buffon to renounce his view that the mountains, valleys and continents visible today were not created at the beginning of the world, but subsequently, and would eventually vanish to be replaced by a slow, endless cycle of new mountains, valleys and continents. The coming of the French Revolution in 1789, Lyell went on to suggest, did nothing to open up geological discussion. On the contrary, there was an apprehensive clamp down by the Church in France on any loosening of accepted religious doctrine that hampered progress.

In later chapters and in the second volume published in 1832, Lyell proposed the view that as landscapes changed through millions of years, so did vegetation and the species that it supported. In this way he was almost suggesting what Darwin was to expand fully almost thirty years later, that species adapted or died according to their fitness for survival in a changing environment. However, Lyell still believed that the species were 'fixed' – that they had not evolved, but were only variable to a certain degree, within fixed limits. In fact, Lyell disagreed bitterly with Darwin when *The Origin of Species* was published, and was only gradually brought round to agree that Darwin's theory was the logical step on from his own.

In his final volume of *The Principles*, Lyell travels back in geological time through the Tertiary era, describing how the landscape changed: how the chalk uplands of the south east English coast had been lifted out of the sea, while at the same time there were sea depositions in the depressions where, millions of years later, the cities of London and Paris would stand. He ended with a resounding reiteration of the eternal recurrence of the world's geological features – mountains would eventually be eroded into sands, valleys would rise, coasts alter, seas dry up or form elsewhere. The ice age was retreating, as it had done twice before, and all living species on the earth would slowly adapt with the changing climate:

"When I first came to the notion . . . of a succession of extinction of species, and creation of new ones, going on perpetually now, and through an indefinite period of the past, and to continue for ages to come . . . the idea struck me as the grandest which I had ever conceived." *The Principles* was Lyell's great life's work. He devoted the rest of his time to travels in the summer with his devoted wife Mary, who was as fascinated by beetles and fossils as he.

From Scandinavia to Scotland, Southern Europe to North America, Charles Lyell travelled with his geological hammer while Mary wrote up their findings to save her husband's short-sighted eyes. During the winter Lyell lectured to the geological society on a vast range of subjects, including glaciers, volcanoes, coalfields, fossil trees and fishes to the geological history of much of North America.

LYELL AND THE 'MISSING LINK'

In 1863 Lyell followed up the great achievement of *The Principles* with the publication of an astonishingly wide-ranging book on the fossil record of man's ancestry: *The Antiquity of Man*. This summarized the most up to date discoveries of human civilization and remains, with special reference to skulls discovered in Liege and Neanderthal, dating from the Pleistocene period: the most ancient so far discovered. Were these skulls the link between ape and man, as Darwin had predicted would eventually be discovered? Darwin looked to Lyell, his lifelong friend and supporter, to endorse his human evolutionary theory, but Lyell proved much more cautious. He suggested that although there were certain ape-like characteristics of the Neanderthal skull, it was definitely human. If any transition from ape to human had occurred, it would have been long before Neander-thal man. Having marshalled the facts, Lyell disingen-uously left his readers to make up their own minds. Darwin was a little peeved, but Lyell had put into a nutshell the great debate which would rage on long after their deaths.

FULL OF YEARS AND HONOURS

Lyell became one of the great Victorian men of science and culture. The whole nation approved of him, and after the publication of *The Antiquity of Man* he was created a baronet. He was so respected that Queen Victoria would summon him to discuss philanthropic educational schemes with him. Much of the political fall-out caused by Darwin's *Origin of Species*, cautiously endorsed by Lyell, had left him unscathed.

In 1873 Lyell was shaken to the core by the unexpected death of his beloved wife, who had shared all his geological adventures with him. Two years later he died as well, to be buried in Westminster Abbey. Lyell's enthusiastic and elegant approach had brought geology out of the shadows to become the central debate of the century.

CHAPTER VIII

(1809 – 1882)
CHARLES DARWIN

In 1859, after twenty seven years of research and agonising internal debate, Charles Darwin published *The Origin of Species*. In this book he put forward a mechanism for evolution that had never been suggested before. It was based on three main ideas: that as there were far more creatures born than could expect to survive, the whole of creation owed its existence to a never ending, brutal struggle. The victors in this struggle were those who would inherit the most favourable variations to suit their environment. If environments changed, the species would have to change too. In this way, new species could arise, and old ones would have to adapt, or die out. It was a never ending process of natural selection which occurred in all living populations, whether plants or animals. Not since the early sixteenth century, when Copernicus proved that it was the earth which moved around the sun, and not vice versa, had there been such a revolution in scientific thinking. Religion and science took up their respective positions in the ring to fight out the natural conclusion of this evolutionary struggle put forward by Darwin: that man, too, had evolved in the same way from animal ancestors. Science, religion and politics would never be the same again.

THE WORLD ACCORDING TO GENESIS

The influence that the biblical account of the formation of the world exercised on the popular imagination was considerable. Some interpreters of the Book of Genesis had worked out that the world was possibly only six thousand years old, and that the species had been separately created, with man appearing last as a distinct and highest form of creation. These convictions began to crumble by the middle of the eighteenth century.

Geologists realised that the natural processes which shaped the world's surface: glaciers, wind and water erosion, volcanic activity – must have taken millions of years. The rock strata showed evidence of catastrophic events such as major earthquakes and upheavals. There was also increasing fossil evidence to show that life on earth must have existed much earlier than had previously been thought. Shells from the sands on the ocean floor were now found on the summits of mountain ranges. This evidence was disputed by some, who suggested that pilgrims to the Holy Land during the Middle Ages must have dropped the shells on their route over the Alps. Despite such brave attempts to uphold the traditional biblical interpretation of creation, disconcerting fossil evidence continued to accumulate. Baron Georges Cuvier announced in 1801 that he had discovered the remains of twenty three species which no longer existed.

These combined discoveries of geology and palaeontology had prompted the great French scientist Lamarck to redraw the development of the animal kingdom like a branching tree, rather than a strict hierarchical ladder. In his *Philosophie Zoologique* published in 1809 he stated that all plants and animals had naturally developed from other living things, without divine intervention. Around the same time, Charles Darwin's grandfather, Erasmus Darwin, realised correctly that all life had originated from the sea, and celebrated the idea in a long poem called *The Temple of Nature* in 1803:

"Organic life beneath the shoreless waves
was born, and nurs'd in ocean's pearly caves."

CHARLES LYELL

Well into the nineteenth century, a view of human evolution was still current which regarded animals merely as "foetal stages of man", and fossils as a system of geological prophecy for the great creation of man to come. By 1830, the geologist Charles Lyell (chapter VII) suggested much more impersonal natural forces at work in the formation of the the earth, and realised that disturbances in the natural balance of world, a changed habitat or climate, would have far-reaching ramifications. Plants and animals would have had to adjust to their changed surroundings, or perish. Lyell's *Principles of Geology* was the great inspiration for Darwin's masterly collation of evidence for his theory of evolution.

THE YOUNG NATURALIST

Into this cauldron of controversy stepped, most unwillingly, the naturalist Charles Darwin. He was born in Shrewsbury in 1809, the son of a well-to-do doctor. Young Charles had enjoyed a happy and indulged childhood, but was not inspired by his school subjects and showed no great aptitude for his lessons. He was much more interested in reading up natural science and in general mischief, once causing his father to exclaim in exasperation," you care for nothing but shooting, dogs and rat catching, and you will be a disgrace to yourself and all your family!"

Darwin gave up his medical studies in Edinburgh, and went to Cambridge to study classics instead, with the intention of becoming ordained. His sense of a Church vocation waned while his knowledge of natural science deepened, and he spent all his time on botanical field trips. By the time Darwin graduated in 1831 he was poised to become that phenomenon to which we owe so much of our botanical knowledge today: the Victorian naturalist. Often a comfortably-off vicar, younger son of a squire or unmarried lady of independent means, these intrepid Victorians set out on perilous trips and netted, pinned, formaldehyded or stuffed the exotic flora and fauna of the expanding Empire.

THE VOYAGE OF THE BEAGLE

Darwin quickly found a similar way to fill up the generous vistas of spare time and money which now stretched before him. He was appointed as an unpaid naturalist on a scientific expedition to South America, Tierra del Fuego, the Pacific, New Zealand, Australia and South Africa. The trip was to take four years, and would change the course of Darwin's life.

Darwin took with him a copy of Lyell's newly published *Principles of Geology*. As The Beagle sailed along the coast of South America Darwin kept meticulous notes of all he saw, and came to agree with Lyell's work. By measuring the rock strata of the coast against sea level he realised that the continents were in a continuous state of flux, and parts of South America were slowly rising. Chile in particular had risen several feet in places after a recent earthquake.

Darwin also discovered many fossil remains on the pampas of Argentina: a vast, extinct member of the sloth family as large as a rhinocerous, and curved teeth of a *Glyptodon* which had been similar to a modern armadillo. Horse teeth were also discovered, similar but subtly different to modern horse teeth. On the Galapagos islands, Darwin studied the giant tortoises and many species of brilliantly-coloured birds which were closely related, yet differed slightly from island to island. Slowly

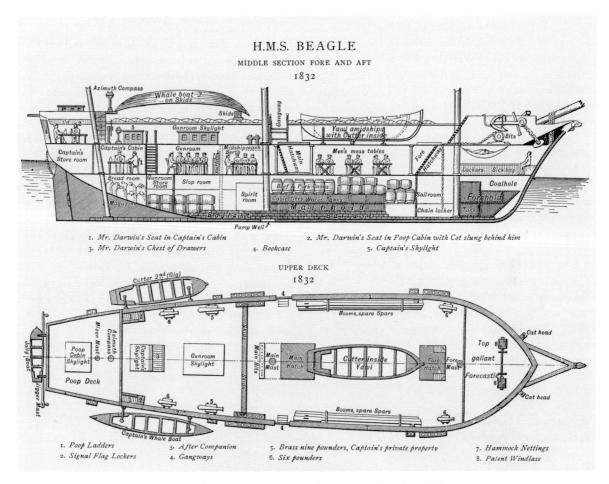

H.M.S. BEAGLE

MIDDLE SECTION FORE AND AFT

1832

1. *Mr. Darwin's Seat in Captain's Cabin*   2. *Mr. Darwin's Seat in Poop Cabin with Cot slung behind him*
3. *Mr. Darwin's Chest of Drawers*   4. *Bookcase*   5. *Captain's Skylight*

UPPER DECK

1832

1. *Poop Ladders*   3. *After Companion*   5. *Brass nine pounders, Captain's private property*   7. *Hammock Nettings*
2. *Signal Flag Lockers*   4. *Gangways*   6. *Six pounders*   8. *Patent Windlass*

A cross-section of H.M.S. Beagle *which took Darwin on his inspirational trip around the world in 1832.*

the tremendous idea of natural selection began to emerge. Some species adapted to their environments, such as the birds of the Galapagos islands, and some had died out altogether in the struggle to survive, like the giant sloth. Man had proved to be the most successful and adaptable animal of all.

What puzzled Darwin was the question of why some species were unique to a certain continent, such as the kangaroos of Australia or the rhea and guinea pigs of South America. With his new understanding of an earth in perpetual movement, Darwin realised that the old idea of species being separately created for each country was too improbable to sustain. Continents had moved, islands thrown up by volcanic activity or separated from the land mass by subsidence. Islands had obviously been

colonised by species of flora and fauna from neighbouring land masses, sometimes thousands of miles away, and species had adapted to local conditions, sometimes subtly and sometimes diverging considerably. Wind and ocean currents had also played a major role in the dispersal of species.

Darwin was seized with the excitement of discovery and filled hundreds of pages of his naturalist notebooks with drawings and observations.

THE THEORY DEVELOPS

When Darwin returned to England he published his dairy of the voyage and other geological observations, in particular on the formation of coral atolls, which Lyell had not quite got right. Corals develop in a warm, limpid sea, attached to land or an island where the sea floor is sinking. In order to maintain access to the sunlight filtering through the water, living coral reefs build upwards at the same speed as the land sinks. Ten years after Darwin's death his theory was proved correct when a borehole was sunk at Funafuti in the Pacific – and coral was discovered to a depth of over one thousand feet.

The principle of evolution had convinced him, and he saw his life's work as the task of amassing further evidence to support this theory.

Darwin next came into contact with the influential ideas of the political economist, Thomas Malthus. Malthusian theory stated that the population always expanded beyond the limits of the world's resources, therefore life was a continual struggle for existence. The weakest and least adaptable did not survive, the strongest formed the next generation. This theory fitted in perfectly with Darwin's developing ideas of natural selection as being the driving force for the evolution of species. As Malthus was a very popular philosopher, fitting in well with the expansionist ethics of the times, Darwin had found himself a powerful ally.

THE FOSSIL RECORD

Meanwhile, Darwin studied, identified and classified fossil barnacles through the Cenozoic era and listed their successive, minute changes through the last sixty five million years, and even earlier in the Mesozoic Era. The evidence for evolution was being meticulously accumulated, although Darwin realised that the fosil record for evolution was very incomplete, and therefore probably the major stumbling block to a general acceptance of his theory. He hoped that the finds of successive generations of paleontologists would fill many of the gaps, but realised that the chances of fossilization and discovery for the vast majority of creatures were very remote.

His work on barnacles gave Darwin the clue to why the fossil record showed that certain species had become extinct. Creatures did not die out due to great world-wide catastrophes, as many geologists had thought. The causes were much more local and various: a change in climate, and vegetation, for example, had caused the horse to adapt its teeth and feeding habits to an increasing pampas vegetation. Ancestors of the horse which adapted more slowly to changing conditions had

The subtle variations of finches from the Galapagos Islands.

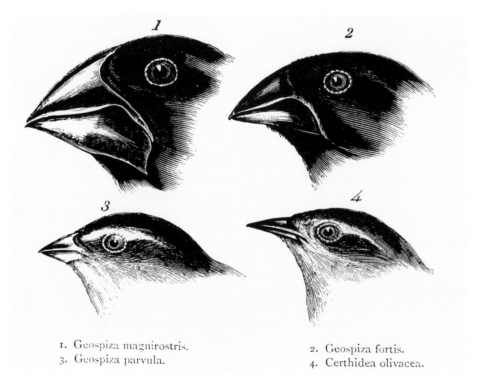

1. Geospiza magnirostris.
3. Geospiza parvula.

2. Geospiza fortis.
4. Certhidea olivacea.

A species of sea lizard unique to the Galapagos Islands.

died out. Competition for food in the sea, or immigrations of a voracious new species, were the probable causes of so many groups of fish disappearing.

Sexual selection, the fierce competition for a mate, was another factor in Darwin's theory of the 'survival of the fittest.' It also explained the brilliant variety of colour in nature, as the brightest and fiercest males competed for the females.

While Darwin was working on barnacles, and developing his thoughts on evolution, he had married his cousin and moved to Down House in Kent. In this idyllic spot, free from financial cares and with plenty of time to read, muse and write, the Darwins produced a happy and noisy brood of children. Darwin seemed in no hurry to change the smooth flow of his life. He had a shrewd idea that once his theory of evolution was published, it would cause such uproar and notoriety that his peaceful life might become a thing of the past. He therefore formally wrote to his wife in 1844 that in case of his sudden death, she should devote £400 to the publication of a draft of the species theory, and that Charles Lyell might be the best publisher for it.

WALLACE'S THEORY

But Darwin was in for a great shock. Out of the blue in June 1858 he received a paper outlining his very ideas on natural selection and the origin of the species, from a completely unknown English naturalist. Alfred Wallace's background had been very different to Darwin's: his

life had been a long struggle against financial difficulty and bad luck. Equipped with only £100 he had set off down the Amazon, collecting rare species of fauna and befriending the gentle Indian tribes, whose simple lifestyles he greatly admired. Several times he had lost the many rare species he had collected for shipping back to English museums. Now in the Indian Spice Islands, after a sleepless, feverish night, Wallace had come to exactly Darwin's conclusions. Knowing Darwin to be interested in the same ideas, he shot off a letter to Kent which shattered Darwin's tranquility:

"I never saw a more striking coincidence; if Wallace had my manuscript sketch written out in 1842, he could not have made a better short abstract!"

There was no time to be lost. Papers by Wallace and Darwin were read at the next meeting of the Linnean society in London, where not an academic feather was ruffled. The following year, after a hasty completion, Darwin published *The Origin of Species*.

"THE VILEST AND BEASTLIEST PARADOX EVER INVENTED"

The Origin was an instant success: everyone clamoured for it, from the scientists and philosophers to railway travellers outside Waterloo station besieging the bookstalls. It was the talk at dinner-tables, in taverns and, not least, the pulpits.

Darwin's years of meticulous research had turned the traditional view of creation on its head. The biblical order of creation was still intact. *The Origin* suggested a world millions of years old, a creation evolving according to natural forces and laws of chance. The astronomer John Herschel spluttered that it was "the vilest and beastliest paradox ever invented . . . absolutely incompatible with the work of God.", and which, most unpalatable of all, had presented man as an animal.

DARWIN'S LEGACY

For all the furore he had created, Darwin was the epitome of the contented, Victorian family man. His home life was happy and impeccably respectable. Sheltering behind the protection of his loving family and friends, giving in from time to time to mild hypochondria, Darwin survived the blasts. In 1871 he published the more forgettable *Descent of Man*, which developed his theory on the origin of man and contained ideas on the superiority of white northern man over negroes or women which fitted in well with the attitudes of the times. By the time Darwin died in 1882, he was a national hero, loved and mourned, and buried with great honours in Westminster Abbey.

"Do not allow yourselves to be misled by the common notion that a hypothesis is unworthy simply because

An 1874 cartoon satirizing the author of the Descent of Man.

it is an hypothesis" warned Darwin's life-long friend, Huxley. The basics of evolution quickly became accepted. Skulls of ancient man, and man's near ancestors were discovered in the Neander valley in Germany, and later in the 1920's and '30's in Southern Africa, from where geologists today believe man originated. The skulls of developing man become larger, accommodating a developing brain, the face becomes flatter, with more level teeth showing a creature whose diet changed from a vegetarian to omnivorous. This increase in protein intake allowed more time for social and mental development. Even two million years ago, primitive tools out of flints had been developed by ancient man.

The dispersal of skulls showed that man had survived the ice ages by changes in hunting patterns, following herds rather than haphazardly stalking them. Darwin's great canvas was being pieced together.

Darwin's had been a great leap forward in our understanding of the world. He had not explained everything: his ideas on heredity were vague and on the wrong track, as Mendel was to prove. To accommodate critics such as the almost omnipotent physicist of the day, Lord Kelvin, he whittled down his estimation of the age of the world. Today we know that the world is tens of millions of years older than Darwin had even initially imagined.

There are still questions that evolution has not been able to address. The fossil record still shows great gaps in the development of species, and suggests that evolution was a far from gradual process. There are unaccountable leaps forward, with species such as man developing at an extraordinarily rapid pace when compared to the millions of years of minute development in other species.

The origin of life, and the world, is still a mystery. The basic living cell from which life originally sprang is a structure of such unbelievable complexity that it is hard to imagine it developing even in the extended time-span of the world that we know today. The latest experiments have proved that the atmosphere of the early earth, together with electric atmospheric charges and the presence of ice would have produced the amino acids and organic molecules which form the basis of DNA – the blueprint of life in the cell. The origins of life are still to be explained, but we owe a great debt to Darwin for pointing us in the right direction.

CHAPTER IX

(1822 – 1884)
FATHER GREGOR MENDEL

It had always been accepted that all living things – plants, animals and humans – take on characteristics from their parents in appearance, build and even character. From this observation the most extraordinary theories arose, which were widely accepted for centuries. The birth of grossly deformed children, for example, was thought to have resulted from cross breeding between man and an animal, with the result that belief in creatures such as werewolves was common in Europe until around the eighteenth century. Gradually, however, as farmers became increasingly skilful in breeding prize animals for specific milk or meat yields, and learnt how to graft fruit trees and cross-fertilize crops to arrive at new strains, the old superstitions fell away. Yet throughout the nineteenth century the scientific principles behind these phenomena continued to elude the most prominent biologists and scientists: even Darwin could offer no convincing explanation.

At this time, the mainstream of scientific thinking in Britain, Europe and America was being convulsed by the new evolutionary theories of Dr Charles Darwin (see chapter VIII). Away from the controversies and almost entirely unobserved, some of the most important research of the century was being carried out in the gardens of an Augustinian monastery in Austria. By 1863 Father Gregor Mendel had painstakingly completed a decade of experiments with pea plants, and the implications of his conclusions were to lay the foundations of a whole new branch of science: genetics. Mendel's theories were so far in advance of contemporary thinking that they were only discovered and recognised by chance, over thirty years later.

Mendel among his fellow monks at the monastery of Altbrunn.

THE SILESIAN GARDENER

The odds against Johann Mendel gaining anything more than the most rudimentary education were very great. He was born in 1822, the only son of Silesian peasants, who lived in a part of the Austrian Empire which is now Czechoslovakia. The Mendels farmed under the semi-feudal conditions still prevalent throughout most of early nineteenth century Europe. Heavy taxes, forced labour (the *corvée*) and repressive political measures were intended to keep the lid on an empire of many nationalities, all struggling for independence.

The only escape from this harsh peasant life was through education, and Johann soon proved himself to be a student of such aptitude that the local schoolmaster pleaded with Johann's father to allow the boy to go on to further education in Troppau. Although it was almost impossible to dispense with the help that Johann could provide on the farm, let alone find the money for board and tuition, his parents decided they must give their son this chance. For six years the growing boy survived on half-rations, and would suffer the after-effects of malnutrition in fatigue, depression and wasted muscles for years to come.

By the time he was twenty Johann had decided that science, especially botany was the love of his life, but how to further his ambitions of study remained a bitter

dilemma. The financial straits of his family were tighter than ever after his father was crippled on one of the days of forced labour for the local landlord, and Johann's sister had already volunteered her dowry to pay for her brother's studies. It seemed he had gone as far as he could, when unexpectedly his professor suggested a solution.

THE MONASTERY OF ST THOMAS

The only route to higher education left to Johann was through the church. The convents and monasteries of nineteenth century Catholic Europe were often re-nowned centres of learning and research, and the Augustinian monastery at Altbrunn (now Brno) was no exception. In particular, the monastery was famed throughout Austria for its botanical museum and gardens, and well-stocked library. The high level of intellectual achievement attained by the community had been fostered by its scholarly Prelate, who prided himself in discovering and nurturing the talents of his monks.

Johann was admitted to the monastery, where his intellectual gifts were quickly appreciated. In 1847 he was ordained a priest, Father Gregor Johann Mendel. It was obvious that his gifts were for teaching and research, although throughout his life, in the world beyond the monastery Mendel would always be treated as a jumped-up intellectual outsider. His lack of a university degree coupled with his highly independent thinking caused him to be endlessly patronised and overlooked. Strictly speaking, he did not even have a right to teach at the high school, and it was only the influence of the Prelate that had secured him the post.

SCIENCE AND POLITICS

Mendel was urged to study for the teaching certificate which would give him legitimacy in the eyes of the school governors. While his papers were generally well received, ironically it was the essay on natural history which met with the disapproval of his examiners.

The monastery library had kept scrupulously up to date with the latest scientific publications, and consequently Mendel was well acquainted with contemporary evolutionary theory, and Charles Lyell's ideas in geology (see chapter VII). However, Austria in 1848 was rocked by violent popular uprisings. The rebellions were uncoordinated and easily crushed by a frightened government, and a wave of reactionism swept the country. Examiners of teachers were in no mood to countenance what they considered to be ungodly and revolutionary new theories in science passed on to the youth of Austria; indeed many eminent professors had not even understood the latest in geological thinking themselves yet. Added to that, Mendel was largely self taught with considerable gaps in his knowledge.

Mendel went on to study science for two years at the university of Vienna, and presented himself for the teaching examination. It soon became apparent that Mendel's close study of the contemporary debates on plant evolution had no support among the conservative examiners. Mendel's patience had finally run out. Pausing in mid-sentence during a viva-voce examination, he asked to be withdrawn from the examinations. From now on, Mendel would go his own way.

THE GARDEN LABORATORY

For a long time, Mendel had been interested in the evolution of plants and animals, and exactly how successive generations passed on their characteristics. It had also been long accepted that different varieties of the same species, when cross-bred, could not be relied on to reproduce the exact characteristics of the parent plants.

This second, hybrid, generation, possessed a great uniformity of colour and size. When the hybrids were cross-bred to produce a third generation, lo and behold the original characteristics of the grandparent generation often made an appearance again. This seemed generally to be the case, whether the hybrids were puppies, pigeons or sweet peas. Occasionally, hybrids were sterile, as when a horse and donkey are crossed to produce a mule.

It was believed that when throw-backs to the first generation occurred, it was entirely at random. Mendel was not satisfied with this explanation. He felt there had to be laws in nature, as in all branches of science, which governed the laws of heredity. Choosing to observe the generations of pea plants because of their quick germination, ease of cross-pollination and fertile hybrids, Mendel began the most immense, painstaking experiment of pea plant breeding which engulfed the whole monastery garden and would take over fifteen years to accomplish.

THE TWENTY YEAR PEA EXPERIMENT

The most difficult part was knowing how to start. Mendel knew that each minute grain of pea pollen carried hundreds of characteristics which determined the eventual plant: whether the seeds would be smooth or wrinkled, the plants tall or short, the flowers red, yellow, orange, pink or white, the peas small or fat, and so on. If he tried to keep track of all these characteristics through successive generations, he would drown in data. But one of Mendel's great qualities was a determinedly methodical approach, and he decided to concentrate on just seven, easily identifiable characteristics, ignoring all the other variations: tall or short plants, flowers at the top or bottom of the plant, the colour of the unripe pod (green or yellow), the shape of the ripe pod (smooth or knobbly), the colour of the seed coat (white or grey), the colour of the seed leaves (green or yellow) and the shape of the ripe seed (round or wrinkled).

Mendel searched far and wide throughout the countryside for pea seeds, and spent two years eliminating the chance hybrids among them. For his experiments he had to be sure that they would all breed true.

Soon the monastery garden was filled with regiments of sticks marking beds of different pea varieties. To each plant was tied several small bags which had been placed

Portrait of a Short-horned Bull by Thomas Weaver. A Splendid example of a prize bull produced by selective breeding techniques long before Mendelian

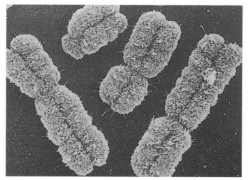

A group of human chromosomes in the nucleus.
Each chromosome consists of a tightly wound ribbon
of D.N.A., in the form of a double helix.

around the cut away stigmas of the pea flowers, to prevent random pollination from different varieties by bees and insects. Mendel artificially pollinated the stigmas with a fine hair brush loaded with pollen from the ripened stamens. By the end of the first stage of his grand plan, he had carried out two hundred and eighty seven cross-pollinations. In the case of crossing wrinkled-seeded plants with smooth-seeded plants, Mendel discovered that the seeds produced from this first hybrid generation, all looked exactly like their round-seeded parent plant and unlike the other. This was the F1 (first filial) generation, and it was already a surprise. Current heredity thinking suggested that the two characteristics would be merged in the offspring.

THE SECOND GENERATION

Mendel's next step was to allow the first pea generation to self-fertilise: what he discovered then was to prove the crux of his heredity theory. The second generation of plants produced seeds which had reverted to the grandparent types: there were both round-seeded and wrinkled-seeded forms. He repeated this experiment hundreds of times, and when counting up the seeds he found that there were three round-seeded forms to one wrinkled-seeded form. This confirmed what Mendel had hoped would be the case: that a simple mathematical law underlay the complexities of heredity. From this result, he gave a new name to the characteristics, such as rounded-seeds which were three times more likely to occur: they were *dominant*. The wrinkled seeds had only

rinciples were understood.

a one in four chance of appearing in the second and subsequent generations, and they were *recessive*.

Mendel realised that each plant had two factors in its cell to pass on the characteristics of roundness or wrinkledness, for example. However, in reproduction, only one factor for any specific characteristic is present in the reproductive cell of the male plant, ready to be joined by a partnering factor in the egg cell of the female plant, so passing on two factors to the next generation. Each living thing, whether plant or animal, receives one factor from each parent to determine every aspect of its eventual appearance. These factors can be both dominant, or both recessive, or one dominant and one recessive. In the case of the pea plants, this would have resulted in dominant rounded seeds, recessive wrinkled seeds, or a mixed pair of factors resulting again in a rounded seed, as it 'swamped' the recssive factor for wrinkledness.

THE KEY TO HEREDITY

Mendel had finally unlocked the secret of heredity. The characteristics of parents were not diluted, or mixed, in their offspring, as was generally thought, but passed on entirely. Different characteristics are transmitted separately: a child can, for example, inherit 'dominant' black hair from one parent and 'recessive' blue eyes from the other.

Sometimes characteristics skip a generation. In 1900 a Swedish scientist called Johannsen gave the name *genes* to the factors which transmit characteristics in the cells, and today we know that these genes are contained in a tightly wound ribbon of information in each cell called *chromosomes*. In a cell so microscopic that it cannot be seen by the naked eye, the ribbon of chromosomes is forty six feet long!

We also know today that sometimes, for no apparent reason, the genes change or *mutate*, giving rise to an entirely new set of factors. In this way, living things are continually changing and diversifying.

THE SCIENTISTS OF BRNO

After thousands of experiments over fifteen years, Mendel wrote up his findings and gave a series of lectures in Brno in 1865. Although his findings were well received as a useful report on hybridisation, that was about the limit of their impact. It is astonishing to reflect that only two years previously, Darwin's *Origin of Species* had been translated into German, and still nobody grasped how Mendel's theories filled part of what Darwin had been unable to explain: the mechanics of heredity. Mendel was not overly troubled, and confided to his friend Niessel in his beloved monastery garden: "My time will come."

Mendel's remaining years were taken up with further complex invesigations into the hybrids of other plants. His eyesight was slowly failing, and he was also increasingly distracted by the business affairs of the monastery and local community. Mendel had been elected abbot, and though there was nothing he would rather have done than work quietly in his garden to the end of his days, as abbot he was automatically elected to the Provincial Assembly of the Austrian government. He was soon dragged into constitutional and tax controversies, making enemies by stubbornly refusing to allow his monastery to pay a new monastic tax to the govenment. For nine years, Mendel pursued his legal claim to tax exemption with the same conviction that had sustained his research into genetics. What finances he had were swallowed up by this defiance of the authorities, as well as in paying the school fees of his nephews, as a recompense to his sister who had given up her dowry for his sake so many years before. His health worsened and his visitors were few. He spent his last years devising chess problems for his nephews to solve when they came to visit, and donated 3,000 guilders to equip a splendid fire station in his native village. He died in January 1884, worn out at the age of sixty one.

POSTHUMOUS FAME

While Mendel had always been known and quoted in his field, which was plant hybridisation, the wider significance of his work lay undiscovered until 1900. Three scientists researching into heredity, evolution and genetic variation rediscovered Mendel's papers which, they claimed, supported theories independently arrived at by themselves. The validity of his principles were quickly tested and proved. A whole branch of science was opening up. Today we have experiments in 'genetic engineering' in plants and animals, and the genetic manipulation of embryos to try and eliminate hereditary disease. The trail from this work leads right back to Mendelin principles.

CHAPTER X

(1749 – 1823)
EDWARD JENNER

For over a thousand years, the smallpox disease was dreaded throughout the world. It was estimated to have killed one in six sufferers, and it is now thought that some of the plagues chronicled in history were in fact epidemics of smallpox, which laid waste to armies and caused whole towns to decay. By the middle of the twentieth century smallpox was finally eradicated from even the remotest regions of the world, and this achievement is largely due to an English country doctor, Edward Jenner.

HEALTH IN THE EIGHTEENTH CENTURY

By the end of the eighteenth century, when Dr. Jenner's invesigations into smallpox were at their height, one in ten of the English population would die of the disease. These figures would not have been very different throughout the world. If smallpox did not carry off the patient altogether, his face was left permanently roughened by the healed scars of the pustules. The invisible threat of the disease was everywhere. One eighteenth century doctor writing on medicine commented:

"Few people would choose even to hire a servant who had not had smallpox, far less purchase a slave who had the chance of dying of the disease, and if an infant happen to be seized with the smallpox upon the mother's breast, who has not had the disease herself, the scene must be distressing. If she continue to suckle the child it is at the peril of her own life; if she wean it in all probability it will perish . . . "

A fashionable precaution for smallpox did exist, crude though it was. It had long been recognised that those who had survived smallpox would never succumb to the disease again. Consequently it became the practice every autumn for old women practitioners to carry nutshells of smallpox pus from house to house, and inoculate all who were willing with a needle-head of pus. The small wound was bound up, and a mild form of the disease would run its course eight days later. This treatment became so fashionable that the princesses of England were inoculated during the epidemic of 1721 –

the treatment having first been tested for safety on a selection of orphans and condemned criminals! Unfortunately this form of inoculation was quite dangerous, and a number of high society victims died. From some pulpits the practice of inoculation was declared to be an invention of Satan, but despite the risks it gradually became accepted everywhere.

THE YOUNG JENNER

The man who would transform the practice of inoculation was born in 1749. Edward Jenner was the sixth and last child of an educated, kindly and prosperous parson in the Gloucestershire village of Berkeley. Very early on in Jenner's life, both his parents died, and this blow would overshadow him for the rest of his life. Soon after this came a second crushing experience which almost cost him his life: his inoculation against smallpox.

By the mid-eighteenth century, those who practised inoculation belived the patient should be well prepared before hand by a terrifying 'health' regime. Young Edward was bled and purged for six weeks, until his strength had almost completely drained away. He was dosed to keep his blood sweet, and his diet was a meagre one. When he was finally inoculated with smallpox his constitution was all but shattered, and the experience was never forgotten.

Edward Jenner did recover, however, and by the time he reached twelve his family decided the best thing was for the young orphan to enter the gentlemanly medical profession. Instead of sending him to Oxford, where he would have gained a university degree but not have learnt very much about medicine, he was apprentice to a local surgeon.

Jenner's first appprenticeship was rudimentary and undemanding, allowing him plenty of time for his other interests in natural history. He became acquainted with traditional ointments and potions as well as the basics of surgery, which even in the late eighteenth century was often a rough and ready practice. Saws and scalpels were the main tools of the trade, and as the necessity for absolute cleanliness was not yet realized, nothing was sterilized. Even basic antiseptics would not make an appearance for another hundred years. Gangrene was common, as compound bone fractures were often amputated. The only anaesthetic was rum, and leeches were used to clean wounds and purge the blood. The leech was the closest the eighteenth century doctor came to cleaning a wound antiseptically. Although it was not known then, the mouths of leeches emit an antispectic fluid that also acts as a local anasthetic. After two hundred years of being shunned, the leech is being taken seriously again by some doctors as an effective cleanser for certain wounds.

HUNTER'S SCHOOL OF ANATOMY

In 1770, Edward went to London to become the pupil of John Hunter at his anatomy school in Jermyn Street. Hunter was a most distinguished surgeon and a Fellow of the Royal Society. His character was eccentric, irreverent, hot tempered and extremely companionable, so that until his death in 1793 Hunter remained Jenner's life-long friend.

Hunter represented the new school of doctors who were strongly convinced of the value of a scientifically based medical training. This was to be based on experimentation, observation, and scrupulous analysis and dissection of dead animals as well as human corpses of all shapes, sizes and diseases. Hunter's pupils were expected to become surgeon-apothecaries – perform operations and prescribe (and often concoct) medicines for their patients. They were the new general practitioners, and based much of their treatment on sensible preventative medicine. If a treatment failed, taught Hunter, it was probably the wrong one and should be abandoned. Nothing should be taken for granted. This was a revolutionary concept to doctors unused to questioning traditional methods, and was to influence Jenner's approach to medical problems quite profoundly.

JENNER THE NATURALIST

Although Jenner and Hunter worked together in harmony, Jenner was no lover of the rough, grimy city that London had become. His real home would always be the countryside, where he had been able to indulge his great interest in birds and fossils. (Jenner was later to write important papers on the breeding habits of the cuckoo.) While in London he met the great naturalist Joseph Banks, just returned from the *Endeavour* voyage with Captain Cook, during which the Pacific Ocean and recently discovered continent of Australia had been charted and surveyed. Jenner was able to help Banks classify a unique collection of mineral and botanical

A Gillray cartoon of 1802, satirizing the popular apprehension that there would be bestial consequences if humans were injected with the cowpox vaccine.

specimens that had broken up during a storm at sea. Jenner was so meticulous and deft that Banks was impressed enough to offer the young student a place on the next voyage, but it was reluctantly declined.

The following year, in 1772, Jenner collected his medical certificates, which included anatomy, surgery, chemistry and midwifery. He had profited from teachers who were ahead of their time, and returned to Berkeley to set up his country practice there.

THE BERKELEY SURGEON

Jenner was a great success from the very start. His reputation for surgical skill grew rapidly, and his sympathetic, unhurried and sensible approach gained him the confidence of all his patients. His life was tasteful, cultured and leisurely; he played the flute, wrote papers on natural history, experimented with organic fertilizers, and finally got married at the late age (for the times) of forty. Worried about his wife's health, Jenner moved his practice to the spa of Cheltenham. As the fashionable clientele there would not want to be treated by a mere surgeon (associated then with treating servants, purging and blood letting), without much

further ado he was awarded a medical degree from St. Andrews University on the recommendation of several eminent doctors.

THE COWPOX CONNECTION

Inoculation against smallpox was an everyday duty, and during the frequent epidemics Jenner found himself becoming increasingly interested in the disease. It was well-known in country circles that milkmaids rarely seemed to catch the dreaded smallpox, because they had often caught the much milder cowpox instead. Nobody made too much of this phenomenon, but Jenner could not let the association go out of his mind. When he returned to his country practice in Berkeley, he became almost obsessive about the idea, to the annoyance of his friends who were used to his jovial, easy-going company. Now whenever Jenner had a spare moment he would visit any cow or milker for miles around that had had cowpox, gradually building up a picture of the disease. He had precise drawings made of cow pox pustules so that the disease could be immediately identified and disinguished from other infections.

By 1796 Jenner had become sure that inoculation

with matter from the milder cowpox pustules, instead of the more deadly smallpox pustules, would be equally effective and certainly less dangerous to the patient. By 1798 he had inoculated several children with cow pox, and subsequently with small pox. In every case, the coxpox inoculation protected the children from any symptom of smallpox. Delighted with his successes, Jenner published his notes and observations in a little book entitled: *An Inquiry into Cause and Effects of the Variolae Vaccinae.*

THE PUBLIC REACTION

Jenner's *Inquiry* was an immediate sensation. "No book so small has been talked of so much" wrote Sir Benjamin Richardson, and soon, inevitably, the controversies arose. The symptoms of smallpox and coxpox could be so similar that it was easy to inoculate the wrong one by mistake, with disastrous results. Supporters of the traditional smallpox inoculation aligned themselves against Jenner and his supporters. Moral objections were raised against the inoculation of humans with the diseases of animals – might this not lead to the developments of bestial characteristics? The cartoonists seized on this idea with glee, while ponderous ripostes were made by Jenner's supporters who wrote that eating animals and drinking milk had not seemed to harm generations of Englishmen until then – so what damage could one small inoculation do?

VACCINATION ACROSS THE SEAS

The word 'inoculation' quickly fell into disuse, being associated with smallpox inoculation. A Plymouth doctor suggested *vaccination*, derived from the Latin word for cow, and this was gratefully accepted by Jenner. A coterie of doctors zealously began to spread the vaccine around the world.

In 1800 the Royal Vaccine Institution was founded in Berlin, and from there institutions spread throughout Europe. The following year Napoleon authorized the opening of an institute in Paris, even though France was at war with England at the time. The Dowager Empress of Russia decreed that the first child in the land to be vaccinated would be endowed with the name of Vaccinoff, transported in a ceremonial coach to St. Petersburg and be given a pension for life.

Vaccines were sent across the ocean to America in quills, or saturated onto lint that was then pressed between two oiled glass plates. For even longer voyages such as to India, children proved the best means of transport. One child would be vaccinated and after about seven days the next would be vaccinated, taking material from the arm of the first, and so on, throughout the whole voyage. South America received the vaccine with particular delight, as the Indian population there had been almost wiped out when smallpox arrived via the Spanish Conquistadores two hundred years before. From the other end of the continent ten Canadian Indian chiefs also sent their gratitude together with a bead belt, and invoked the Great Spirit to watch over Brother Jenner for ever.

FINAL REWARDS

In England, Parliament decided to award Dr. Jenner £10,000 for his tremendous contribution to public health, which was beginning to be urgently needed. Jenner was no longer a general practitioner, as his time was now taken up with the promotion of vaccination around the world. Everyone knew how to perform a vaccination, so there were no extra fees there. When Jenner returned to his house in Berkeley after the adulation and social round of London, he became a country doctor again, setting up a vaccination hut – grandly named the Temple of Vaccina – in his garden.

Overwork and continued controversies over his vaccine began to make him ill-tempered, and the continued ill health of his beloved wife troubled him deeply. Catherine Jenner died in 1815, and her husband survived her by seven years, living quietly at his Gloucestershire home. When Jenner died in 1823, a magnificent funeral at Westminster Abbey was waived by his family in favour of a simple grave in his home village.

THE END OF SMALLPOX

Through the long years of campaigning for vaccination, Jenner had never substantially added to his discovery. But Jenner was determined that one day his dream of eradicating smallpox entirely would be achieved. In 1967 the World Health Organisation took up his challenge to stamp out smallpox everywhere, and this was finally achieved by 1977, with the last recorded case occurring in Somalia.

CHAPTER XI

(1822 – 1895)
LOUIS PASTEUR

Throughout the world, 'pasteurization' has become a household name. Most children in the developed countries today have never drunk 'unpasteurized' milk straight from the cow, and might feel inexplicably nervous if expected to do so. Pasteurization was named after the great French scientist, Louis Pasteur, and was just one of his many lasting achievements. He was also a pioneer in the study of crystals and immunology, and famous for inventing a vaccine against the fatal rabies as well as for pioneering vaccination against anthrax in cattle. Pasteur will always be counted among the greatest of French national heroes, not only because he was a dedicated scientific genius, but because his motivation seemed to be a love of humanity as well as an overriding patriotic love of his country. Today his name honours thousands of French streets and houses, and the Pasteur Institute which he founded is one of the world's leading research centres into disease.

THE TANNERY IN THE JURA

Louis Pasteur was the great-grandson of a serf, who had been awarded his freedom together with four pieces of gold after the French Revolution. Louis' father had been a sergeant-major in Napoleon's army, and his valour had earned him the Legion of Honour. Throughout his life, Jean Joseph Pasteur remained devoted to the memory of his Emperor and the glory that had been the First Empire. It was a deep, conservative patriotism which was handed on to his only son, Louis, and which would, in turn, direct his tremendous talents.

The Pasteurs were poor tanners living in the foothills of the Jura mountains in France. They were hardworking, idealistic and devout parents, not possessing much education, but anxious that their children should educate and develop themselves as much as possible. Louis was born on 27th December, 1822. From his early days he displayed a dogged temperament and serious frame of mind, striving at his studies and taking his duties as advisor and protector of his sisters seriously to an almost comic degree.

He did not seem to be particulary outstanding at school, but during his teens one talent began to manifest itself very powerfully. Louis was an excellent artist, and completed many pastel drawings of his parents and friends. Until he was nineteen he planned to study art, but suddenly he dropped the idea, determined to concentrate only on science. His love of art never wavered, but with that single-mindeness that grew stronger over the years it was pushed aside, along with almost every other outside distraction.

THE LIGHT OF CRYSTALS

The work that Pasteur later described as having been the great personal triumph of his life was also the least famous. Like art, crystallography was a subject to which he longed to devote himself, but public demands on his skills were to channel him into other fields. As a young twenty-five year old researcher he had conducted an impressive series of investigations into crystalline structure, under the most difficult and homemade laboratory conditions. Pasteur discovered a new pair of organic compounds which were almost identical, apart from the way their surfaces were 'optically active' – that is, their ability to reflect light. One half of the compound reflected light to the left, the other, to the right. Each pair was therefore a mirror image of the other. The broader conclusions he drew from this very specialised research was that only living agents could produce asymmetric compounds which were optically active. He believed a close study of such molecules would further unravel the mystery of life's biological origin – a concept that had always fascinated him. Pasteur was so delighted he danced out of the laboratory and threw his arms around the first person he met: a spontaneity that his colleagues in later years would have difficulty in attributing to the silent, sad-eyed director of their research.

THE PROBLEM OF SOUR WINE

Pasteur was soon compelled to give up his studies in crystals. He was showered with honours and prizes, and became professor of chemistry at Lille in northern France. His work was directed into the industrial application of chemistry, and this line of research was soon to dominate his life. "There are not two different kinds of science", he would declare, "there is science and there are the applications of science."

On the invitation of an industrialist, M. Bigo, Pasteur began his long investigations into the problem of alcohol becoming comtaminated by other substances during fermentation, which turned the wine or beer sour. From his earlier experiments, Pasteur was convinced that fermentation was a process involving *living* substances, or 'ferments' as he called them. Whether these 'ferments' were yeast, or the most common transformation of sugar into lactic acid (which turns milk sour), their action was speeded up or slowed down according to the acidity, neutrality or alkalinity of the fermenting liquid. Pasteur further pondered the question. If, as he suspected, these organic changes were caused by tiny living microbes, where did they come from? Were they in the air, waiting for favourable conditions to multiply in the food, or were they generated by the lifeless food itself, springing from nowhere – as most scientists, apart from Pasteur, believed? Pasteur was soon to find himself embroiled in this academic controversy of the 'spontaneous generation' of living organisms as he pursued his researches, but he was to prove his point in the most elegant way.

THE SWAN-NECKED FLASK

Pasteur moved to Paris to take charge of scientific studies at the *Ecole Normale*, where the government allowed him what for scientists then was the unheard of luxury of a full time research assistant. His other facilities were rickety in the extreme – he set up a makeshift laboratory in a few spare attic rooms, with a cupboard under the

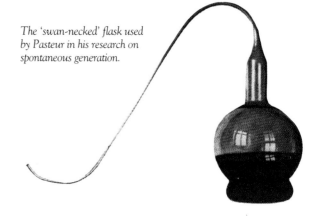

The 'swan-necked' flask used by Pasteur in his research on spontaneous generation.

Pasteur dictating the day's research on silkworm disease to Madame Pasteur in the Cevennes, in 1867.

stairs serving as an incubating room. This was so tiny that he had to crawl inside on his hands and knees, but Pasteur was undaunted and spent hours hunched up over his flasks in the cupboard.

One of his most simple and decisive experiments was to settle the question of 'spontaneous generation' for a long time to come. He poured some meat broth into a glass flask and heated the flask's neck, so that it became pliable and could be drawn out into the shape of an 'S'. The broth was heated until it boiled, forcing air out through the 'swan' neck. As the broth cooled again the condensation in the 's' bend served as a filter for any impurities in the returning air, leaving a sterile broth in the flask. Pasteur prepared dozens of these flasks. When

he broke the necks of certain flasks, the broth turned mouldy within a few days as microbe-contaminated air came back into contact with it. In the flasks that remained unbroken, however, the broth remained as clear and fresh as ever – as it still is to this day, in the flasks that remain at the Pasteur Institute. Pasteur had proved that micro-organisms do not generate spontaneously in sterile surroundings. As Pasteur himself explained it in a famous lecture at the Sorbonne in 1864, no mould grew in the sterile broth "because I have kept it from the only thing man does not know how to produce; from the germs in the air, from Life, for Life is a germ, and a germ is Life."

Once it was understood that microbes could not arise

spontaneously out of a sterile environment, it became possible to tackle the industrial problem of food and drink preservation. A problem which had plagued wine producers for centuries was the high incidence of wine and beer fermenting badly in the bottle, and becoming spoiled. In 1864 the Emperor of France himself asked Pasteur to see what he could do about it.

When Pasteur examined a few drops of soured wine under a microscope, he observed micro-organisms which were similiar to the lactic acid bacteria he had noticed in previous experiments. Impurities which affected the fermentation process were obviously getting into the grape juice, because grapes were grown in the open air. In the case of beer, the yeast used to ferment the liquid was often impure, and this again caused problems. Although the cases of bad fermentation could be drastically reduced by using pure yeast in sterilized vats, the liquids were still in contact with air during the manufacturing process. Pasteur wanted to eliminate all risk of souring, and he began to experiment cautiously with heating the wine to destroy what organisms remained. As a lover of wine he was most concerned that its bouquet should not be spoiled during this process, and little by little he discovered that heating a wine in the bottle to 55 degrees centigrade would preserve it indefinitely. This process was equally effective in preserving any liquid. Pasteur had caused a revolution in food production, and the invention quickly swept across Europe to America where huge 'pasteurization' factories were built. With characteristic generosity, he released the patents for the new 'Pasteurization' process to the French people, and he went on to help design industrial equipment for pasteurization on a wide scale.

THE SILKWORM DISEASE

By now, Pasteur was being regarded as the ultimate 'fixer' for whatever problems were assailing French industry. The next to call on him for help were the silk weavers. A mysterious disease was ravaging the silkworm nurseries, destroying the worms. What had been one of the most prestigious of French industries was almost in ruins. Pasteur studied the silkworm disease for five years, from 1865 to 1870, living mainly in an old stone house and makeshift laboratory in the mountainous silk worm region, the *Cevennes*.

During this time two of his young daughters died, as

An engraving of Pasteur testing the hydrophobia vaccine on rabbits at the Ecole Normale in Paris, in 1884.

well as his father who had inspired him so much as a boy. Pasteur's wife and remaining little daughter came to the Cevennes to help Pasteur in his work – his daughter contributed to the cause by hiding her father's pens as often as possible so that he would at least stop work to eat. By now Pasteur was practically at the end of his strength, if not his determination. Worn out by sorrow and overwork, he almost died of a cerebral haemorrhage which permanently paralysed his left side. However, he struggled on and established that the silkworms were affected by not one but two diseases, one caused by a parasite in the worm and one by the diseased grain it fed upon. Pasteur wasted valuable strength in violently defending his ideas from many detractors, especially the grain merchants who found themselves compromised by Pasteur's discoveries. However in the teeth of opposition, Pasteur established an education programme for the silk

weavers to enable them to raise healthy silkworms and screen out diseased cocoons. The industry was saved, and Pasteur had already begun to apply his studies on silkworm disease to the two great discoveries of his later years.

FROM CHICKEN CHOLERA TO ANTHRAX

During the nineteenth century, the most infectious and fatal disease to affect cattle was anthrax. There was no known cure, although it had been suspected that the disease was caused by bacteria. This 'germ theory' was still regarded with the utmost suspicion by most scientists, and it was finally Pasteur and a brilliant young German, Robert Koch, who proved that anthrax had a bacterial cause.

Koch proved that bacteria present in the tissues of sick animals would multiply rapidly in serum, and infect any healthy animal injected with this serum. Some scientists objected that the serum might have become contaminated by other means, so Pasteur cultivated the

anthrax bacillus in a sterile environment from a drop of infected blood. He distilled this drop to such a dilution that not a molecule of the original blood remained in his final solution: the bacillae, however, had been cultivated and multiplied to such an extent that the distilled liquid killed rabbits and guinea pigs as promptly as the infected blood had done. This was proof enough for Pasteur that bacteria in the animal tissues caused anthrax, but how could it be cured, and how could he make the sceptics accept his discoveries?

The cure for anthrax occurred to Pasteur in a flash of inspiration after a hot summer working on a new virulent strain of chicken cholera. The cholera bacillae had been cultured in the laboratory ready to be injected into chickens, but Pasteur's work had been held up over the summer. When he did get around to injecting the chickens in autumn, to his great surprise most of the chickens survived after an initial infection.

From his knowledge of Edward Jenner's pioneering work with smallpox vaccination half a century earlier (see chapter X), Pasteur realised that chickens had become accidentally 'vaccinated' as well. (Jenner's term had referred to cows, but the process worked equally well with chickens, and the name was to stick). Over the summer the neglected cholera cultures had become weakened, and had acted as a vaccine instead of killing the chickens outright. Pasteur had made a great step forward: instead of accidentally finding the right vaccine for a disease, as Jenner had done, Pasteur now knew that vaccines could be produced in the laboratory.

THE OPEN-AIR INOCULATION SHOW

It was a short step to produce an anthrax vaccine: if the bacillae were cultivated for a few days at a high temperature, they became sufficiently attenuated, or weakened to use as a vaccine. The time had come to silence Pasteur's critics once and for all, and he began to plan a big public inoculation experiment to which the international press would be invited. The event promised to become the sensation of the year. On 5th May 1881 at a farm near Paris, twenty four sheep, one goat and six cows were inoculated with Pasteur's attenuated anthrax vaccine. The dose was repeated twelve days later, and twelve days after that the animals were injected with a potentially lethal pure anthrax culture. A control group of twenty nine animals which had not been previously vaccinated was also injected.

Two days later an anxious Pasteur arrived at the farm – to be greeted by the cheers of spectators. While the control group was already half dead of anthrax, with several sheep expiring at the feet of London journalists later that day, every vaccinated animal was alive and well. Elated by the outstanding success of a demonstration that might have ridiculed him before the world, Pasteur arranged for similiar demonstrations to take place throughout France and abroad. It seemed that Pasteur's renown could climb no higher, but there was one great triumph to come.

THE CONQUERING OF RABIES

The next challenge the great scientist chose to overcome was rabies: perhaps the most terrifying sickness known to man. Nobody ever recovered after being bitten by a rabid animal, and the death of the foaming, thirst-maddened victim was an unforgettable horror to all who witnessed it. The same principle of immunization might work again with rabies, he thought, but dare he inject a human being with an experimental vaccine made from the deadly virus?

Pasteur would cross that bridge when he came to it; for the present he began to make a vaccine out of the spinal cords of rabbits which had died of rabies. He had discovered that by keeping the spinal cord material for two weeks in sterile dried air it became so attenuated as to be almost non-virulent. As the disease develops slowly in animals as well as men, Pasteur injected dogs with the vaccine over several weeks to allow resistance to develop. As with the anthrax cattle, the dogs then survived even when they were injected with the most virulent concentration of the virus. All that was lacking now was a human experiment.

The dilemma was unexpectedly solved in 1885 when a young boy called Joseph Meister was brought to Pasteur suffering from rabid dog bites all over his body. Doctors gave him up as a hopeless case – within a month he would display the fatal symptoms of rabies, and die. Although the patient had nothing to lose by trying out the new vaccine, it was with his heart in his mouth that Pasteur gave him twelve successive injections of spinal cord vaccine, each more virulent than the last. The terrible disease never developed, and Joseph returned to his home in Alsace in perfect health.

THE BEGINNING OF VACCINATION

The defeat of rabies was perhaps Pasteur's crowning success. People flocked to Pasteur's laboratory from all over the world – the Tsar of Russia even awarded the great scientist with a diamond cross and showered grants on the Pasteur Institute. A year later over two thousand people had received the rabies vaccine, and new techniques against viral diseases such as yellow fever were being developed.

Pasteur's success rate was not total, however – sometimes the disease was too far developed for the vaccination to take effect, and in a few cases the dosage of vaccine was not intensive enough to save the patient. Arguments for and against Pasteur's new method of immunisation raged, sometimes bitterly, for years, but increasingly these controversies faded into the background. Within a few years, the principle of immunisation had become accepted as a law of nature, and a new science was born.

THE FINAL YEARS

Pasteur was now an old and frail man, loved and honoured not only in his own country but throughout the world. For his seventieth birthday in 1892 a great festival was organised in his honour at the Sorbonne in Paris, where Pasteur was presented with a medal inscribed: "To Pasteur on his seventieth birthday, with grateful thanks from France and Humanity."

Dearer than that to his heart was the nationwide subscription set up to finance the *Institute Pasteur* – a research institute in Paris which would allow scientists to continue investigations into rabies and other infectious diseases. All his life Pasteur had argued for the need for France to invest in science as a great national endeavour, and France responded magnificently. Donations to fund the Institute came from even the smallest hamlets the length and breadth of the country.

Pasteur died in 1895, and in a fit of patriotic fervour a few years later his countrymen actually named him as the greatest Frenchman who ever lived. Apart from his pioneering work, he had encouraged a sense of national pride in the state support of scientific research. Today the Pasteur Institute in Paris is one of the world's leading research centres into disease, wrestling with such modern catastrophes as AIDS – a challenge which would have been worthy of the great Pasteur himself.

CHAPTER XII

(1881 – 1955)
SIR ALEXANDER FLEMING

The discovery of antibiotics – substances from living organisms which kill germs without harming the body's defences – was one of the great milestones in the history of medicine. Even fifty years ago there was still no effective treatment for deeply infected wounds, and infections within the body.

The extraordinary properties of the rare mould penicillin were discovered by the Scotsman Alexander Fleming in 1928 almost by accident. Even so, at the time, penicillin did not seem to represent any tremendous breakthrough in science. It took over a decade of delay and painstaking research in Oxford by a separate team of chemists under Professor Florey, to refine penicillin and perform the conclusive tests. By then, in 1942, the world was at war, and the full potential of the 'wonder drug' for healing previously incurable infections, diseases and burns, dawned on an astounded public. Although it was Fleming who became a world hero, he modestly spoke for all the scientists involved:

"We certainly live in wondrous times, and when penicillin first came to light neither I nor anyone else had the slightest conception of the enormous influence that it and the later antibiotics would have on medical practice. It is an enormous gratification to have had a hand in this beneficent revolution."

THE FLEMINGS OF AYRESHIRE

The Nobel-prize winning doctor was born in 1881, one of the six children of a Scottish hill farmer near Darvel, in South West Scotland. Life on their high, remote family farm was divided into the rhythms of the farming year: lambing in the early spring, shearing and peat cutting in the summer. In addition, the Fleming children would walk eight miles a day to their little moorland school, where nine or ten pupils sat around a peat fire to do their lessons. It was during these long walks with his brothers and sisters that Alexander acquired the habit of observing minutely all the natural details around him.

Although it was a rigorous childhood, it was not

unusual by the standards of the times, and the family was a close and happy one. All the Flemings remaining in affectionate contact throughout their lives. The children were intelligent, and three brothers were destined for highly successful professional careers in London. Knowledge of such a future would have astounded them, and their community: few dreams seemed possible beyond the heathered moors of Ayreshire.

Alec was a clever boy to whom learning came disconcertingly easy. He had an impish sense of fun and games which was most often hidden behind an often disconcertingly silent demeanour. The medical career that would make him a household name throughout the world had not yet even entered his head, however; that was too remote an ambition for an impecunious farmer's son. By the time he was sixteen Alec had joined his brothers who had moved to London, and enrolled himself as a shipping clerk. This was a dreary time for him, and was only alleviated by a great stroke of fortune which would transform the lives of all the Fleming boys: the receipt of a legacy of £250 from their uncle's will. It was Alec's brother Tom, already a doctor, who suggested that medicine might suit him better than shipping. Without any tremendous enthusiasm or inkling of what the extraordinary consequences would be, Alec agreed.

BACTERIOLOGY AND THE FIRST WORLD WAR

Fleming completed his medical degree at St. Mary's Hospital, London, winning almost every prize and medal that presented itself. Despite qualifying as a surgeon in 1909, he decided to continue his work in the laboratory of Sir Almroth Edward Wright, one of the foremost bacteriologists of the day and a pioneer in the field of vaccines.

Despite the work of Lister and Pasteur, (see chapter X) the war against bacteria was still barely understood. Although he had enlisted tremendous public support, Almoth Wright had battled against an unshakeable official mistrust when he offered to prepare vaccines for the British troops: the army medical authorities were more worried by the body's reaction to vaccination,

A wounded soldier carried through the mud of no-man's land. Fleming regarded his research into antiseptics during the First World War in France as being the most satisfying of his whole career.

which often rendered the soldier unfit for several days. The result was that many troop ships departing for the Boer War in 1901 were ordered to throw caseloads of Wright's vaccines overboard into the Channel. Thousands of unvaccinated soldiers died of typhoid on the South African veld. The outcome of this tragedy was that by the time the First World war broke out in 1914, the medical authorities had bowed to the inevitable. For the first time, the whole of the British army and navy were vaccinated against typhoid.

THE SEARCH FOR ANTISEPTICS

Fleming spent the First World War in makeshift laboratories in Boulogne, helping Wright to identify gas gangrene and tetanus bacteria and trying to find more efficient antiseptics. Until then, harsh antiseptics such as carbolic acid and iodine were the best weapons doctors possessed for treating infected wounds, but they were useless for deep, jagged wounds where bacteria hid and antiseptics could not reach. Worse still, they discovered that these antiseptics destroyed the white blood cells that were part of the body's natural immune system and therefore actually encouraged the spread of infection. Again, these were not conclusions that made Wright popular with many of his medical colleagues.

THE TEARS THAT HEAL

The more Fleming pondered the problem, the more it seemed that the natural immune system of the body was much more powerful than had been previously suspected, and that somehow this system should be harnessed in the fight against internal infections.

One November evening in 1921, as Fleming was clearing up around his usual clutter of tubes and mouldy culture plates, he noticed something rather strange. One plate was covered with golden-yellow colonies of bacteria. In the vicinity of a two-week old blob of mucus from Fleming's nose, there were no bacteria at all. Fleming excitedly prepared a cloudy, yellow solution of the bacteria and added some fresh nasal mucus to it. The young baterologist Dr Allison who was working with Fleming at the time described what happened next:

"To our surprise the opaque suspension became in the space of less than two minutes as clear as water . . . it was an astonishing and thrilling moment."

The bacteria that had been destroyed by the drop

from Fleming's nose was the very rare *micrococcus lysodeikticus*, which had contaminated Fleming's plate by chance, some think by floating through the open window from the London street outside. It turned out to be uniquely vulnerable to the natural anti-bacterial agent which Fleming discovered in his nose-drop. If Fleming had contaminated his slide with usual swabs from human infections, it is likely he would never have observed this effect – as it was, Fleming never found micrococcus lysodeikticus in a naturally occurring state again. Fleming called the anti-bacterial agent lysozyme, after the bacterium which it destroyed so effectively, and found that it could destroy 75% of air-bourne bacteria by 'ingestion'. It existed in tears (which drain into the nose), saliva, blood serum, sperm, pus and even fingernails, in animals as well as humans, and was essential to life. When these natural defences broke down, at death, bacteria invaded and consumed the body. Certain virulent strains of bacteria such as those causing pneumonia, tuberculosis and typhoid, however, were unaffected by lysozyme.

It seemed to Fleming that he had made an important step towards discovering how the perfect antiseptic would work. He was so excited at the thought that he reportedly described the discovery of lysozyme as the best work of his life! Sadly he was such a bad lecturer – mumbling, monotonous and uninspired – that his listeners at the Medical Research Club the following month remained entirely unimpressed, and the announcement of his discovery passed without comment. Fleming was not a man to depend on outside encouragement. Over the next few years, he prepared and incubated thousands of slides to observe the effects of bacteria, his keen eye alert to the minutest changes. On 3rd September, 1928 another remarkable series of chances led to the most important discovery of all. Fleming had just returned from a month's holiday and was busy clearing his workbench of old slides, dumping them into trays of disinfectant. On one slide on top of the pile, miraculously just clear of the disinfectant which would have destroyed the cultures on it, was a blob of mould, surrounded by a zone cleared of bacteria. The mould turned out to contain a rare anti-bacterial agent, penicillin, and must have grown from a chance spore landing on the plate before Fleming sowed a culture of bacillae. If it had landed on the plate after the bacillae had grown, it would not have had the same effect. Sensing something extremely significant had occurred through this chance, Fleming excitedly photographed and preserved the plate.

The penicillium mould had been identified as far back as 1882 by Lister as an antibacterial agent, but, as Fleming was soon to discover, isolating the rare penicillin mould from the thousands that existed was no easy task. Initially, the discovery fell rather flat, especially as Fleming's collleagues were used to him, over the years, showing them interesting bits of moulds and cultures. Added to that, his habitual reserve had long made him notoriously bad in communicating any sense of excitement to others.

Fleming continued with experiments and found that crude penicillin, obtained from meat broth, took over four hours to kill bacteria in the test tube, while it could be destroyed in less than half that time by the body. It was also very sensitive to temperature changes and acidity. As he and his colleagues were not chemists, and resources were scarce, Fleming did not press on with his initial experiments and used the bacteria-killing properties of penicillin mainly to isolate penicillin-resistant

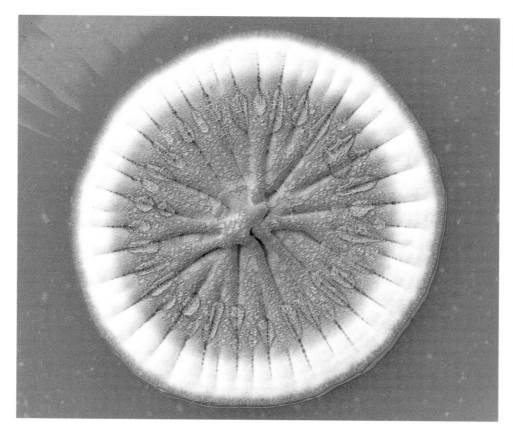

A culture of the rare Penicillium Notatum *isolated by Fleming in 1928.*

viruses for vaccines more quickly and efficiently.

There was another reason why Fleming may not have continued with testing penicillin. The science of chemotherapy (trying to cure infectious diseases by chemical substances) was still part of a highly controversial medical debate. After their experiences with the effect of antiseptics on wounds during the First World War, Fleming and Wright had strong reservations about chemotherapy, and the subject was more or less taboo in Fleming's department. He was more concerned to press on with his work on vaccines.

FLOREY'S BREAKTHROUGH

Despite a desperate lack funding due to the looming Second World War, further research on penicillin was initiated in the late 1930's by an Australian biochemist, Professor Florey. He and a research colleague, a young German refugee biochemist, Ernst Chain, were not, at first, exclusively concerned with penicillin: it was just one of a variety of bacteria-inhibiting substances they had been researching. But its properties were intriguing, and they continued with experiments that Fleming had not tried. They soon discovered that penicillin did not affect the behaviour of mature bacteria, but inhibited the normal development of new bacteria.

What Fleming had also not tried was to give penicillin by mouth and injection to animals. It was discovered that the drug is destroyed in the stomach, making the oral route useless. In May 1940, however, they made a wonderful discovery. Repeated injections of penicillin into mice would overcome a potentially lethal dosage of virulent bacteria. Mice could be protected against infection, but what about humans, who were 3,000 times larger?

With industrial chemists as yet unwilling to enter financial risks with penicillin, its manufacture in Florey's laboratory was painstakingly slow and complicated. Florey turned his department into a penicillin factory to obtain sufficient supplies for the first tests on human patients. The penicillin produced by Florey's laboratory was now around twenty times stronger than had been previously achieved. The results were dramatic. Patients with huge abcesses, eye infections, meningitis, bone and urinary inflammations all either recovered completely or improved at an unprecedented rate. At this stage, however, it was still unclear exactly how much penicillin

to administer, and for how long, and some patients died because the course of precious penicillin they were given ended too soon.

FLEMING'S RETURN TO PENICILLIN

Fleming was very excited, and possibly a little disconcerted by the developments. He sprang into action, and when an employee of his brothers' optical firm fell ill with acute meningitis, he contacted Florey for a sample of the refined penicillin. Without waiting for the results of animal tests (which was just as well, as the animal in question died under the treatment) he courageously injected penicillin into the spinal fluid of the dying man. Less than a month later, the patient walked out of the hospital, completely cured.

The Americans awoke to the potential of penicillin very quickly. War casualties were mounting, and the new drug was proving miraculous in a wide variety of serious illnesses: from chronic infections, including diptheria and pneumonia, to burns. The discovery that gonorrhoea, (which was depleting troops in North Africa more quickly than Rommel) succumbed to penicillin within twelve hours finally convinced the British War office. A leading article in the Times broke the story in August 1942, and the press went wild. The euphoria irritated Professor Florey who shunned the publicity as much as possible, with the result that the more amenable Fleming became increasingly credited with the lion's share of the glory. While Fleming enjoyed the publicity, he was unhappy at the personal element of the developing 'Fleming myth', and tried his best to credit the essential contribution of the Oxford team.

THE NOBEL PRIZE

The press had discovered their penicillin hero with his rags to riches struggle, and they were not about to dilute a good story. Honours were heaped on Fleming's head. A "penicillin train" – a travelling exhibition on the Great Western Railway – toured Britain, and invitations poured in, inviting Fleming to make speeches around the world. The ultimate honour was not long in following, and on 10th December 1945, the Nobel Prize for Medicine was jointly conferred on Fleming, Florey and Chain for their extraordinary faith and tenacity in bringing penicillin to the world. In its wake would come a revolution in the treatment of disease.

CHAPTER XIII

(1736 – 1819)

JAMES WATT

As the Industrial Revolution spread out from Britain in the eighteenth century it gradually transformed the pattern of economic life throughout the world. Water power and wind power, which had been used for centuries to supplement human muscle and the horse, were no longer enough; the change from rural crafts to large-scale industry required a new source of power.

James Watt is sometimes thought to have "invented" the steam engine, but in fact simple engines were already in use before he was born. His great achievement was to transform these primitive, inefficient engines so as to provide a source of cheap and abundant power. Watt was not only one of the greatest "prime movers" of the Industrial Revolution, but his work also changed our outlook on the world by giving mankind, for the first time in history, real control over the forces of nature.

THE FIRST STEAM ENGINES

The original engines were "atmospheric engines" in which the pressure of the atmosphere forced the piston down a cylinder, using the steam to produce a vacuum rather than to provide the power stroke. They worked very simply, just like a village pump; but instead of a human hand pushing the handle down, they used steam in a cylinder.

In 1673 Christopher Huygens had suggested that gunpowder could be used to produce the vacuum. He made a working model, and was acclaimed for devising a peaceful and constructive use for gunpowder, but his engine was not a practical proposition. Huygens' assistant, Denis Papin, suggested that it would be simpler and safer to use steam instead of gunpowder to produce a vacuum, and in 1690 he produced the first plans for a practical engine.

Boulton and Watt's Birmingham factory where the first steam engine was developed.

His idea was based on the fact that when water boils and changes to steam it expands to take up many hundreds of times its original volume. If a cylinder is filled with steam and then cooled, the steam will condense into a few drops of water, leaving a vacuum. The pressure of the atmosphere will then force the piston down to fill this vacuum and could provide a powerful pumping action. Papin worked on this idea for many years, but at that time the process of industrialisation was slower in France and he received little practical or financial support.

A similar plan was patented by Thomas Savery in 1698, and he set up a partnership with Thomas Newcomen to develop the idea. Their first working engine was built in 1712, and by the middle of the eighteenth century hundreds of "Newcomen engines" were in use, mainly to pump water from mines. This was an important first step, but it was not yet the answer to the growing need of the Industrial Revolution for a source of economical and versatile power.

James Watt was born in Greenock, in the west of Scotland in 1736. His father was a carpenter and as a boy Watt spent much of his time in the workshop, showing great practical abilities from an early age. His family was not rich enough for him to be able to continue his education, so he was sent to Glasgow to become apprenticed to a mechanic. In 1755 he went to London to learn the craft of Mathematical Instrument Making and in 1757 he returned to Glasgow as an instrument maker for the University. His skill and quickness of mind soon brought him to the attention of members of the university and he developed an important friendship with Joseph Black, the professor of Chemistry. Black was to give him much support and assistance in these early years and was also able to fill many of the gaps in his knowledge of science. His business did well and in 1764 he married his cousin Margaret.

THE NEWCOMEN ENGINE

The University owned a model Newcomen engine, but it was broken and had been sent to London for repairs. James Watt first heard about this "fire machine" in 1759 and was impatient to see it. While waiting for its return, he learned as much as he could from books and by carrying out experiments using a syringe as a cylinder. After long delays it was still unmended, and at Watt's insistence, it was eventually returned in 1763.

Watt soon got the engine into working order, but he came to the important conclusion that the principle behind it was faulty, and that this was a severe limitation on the practical use or further development of such engines. The main problem was that at every stroke of

the piston, the cylinder had to be cooled in order to condense the steam so as to create a vacuum. It then had to be re-heated so that more steam could be introduced for the next stroke. After running for a short while the model exhausted all the water in its boiler; and, what even more serious, real working engines of this type were wasting much of the fuel in just re-heating the piston instead of producing power.

At first he tried making the cylinder out of wood instead of brass, in an attempt to reduce the waste of

A design for a 'Newcomen' pumping engine used in collieries at the end of the eighteenth century.

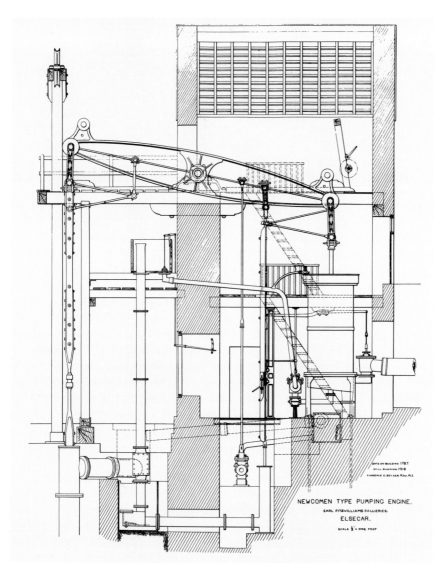

DATE ON BUILDING 1787
STILL RUNNING 1918
CLARENCE O. BECKER M.Am. M.E

NEWCOMEN TYPE PUMPING ENGINE.
EARL FITZWILLIAMS COLLIERIES.
ELSECAR.
SCALE ½" = ONE FOOT

A romantic depiction of Watt being inspired by a steam kettle, by the Scottish artist J. E. Lauder

heat, but this made very little improvement – and the engine still needed large amounts of cold water to cool the steam. Watt discussed the problem with Joseph Black, but they were unable to find any way of increasing the engine's efficiency. The dilemma was that for maximum power all the steam has to be condensed, and for this the cylinder has to be cooled right down. But for the maximum economy, it has to be kept hot all the time no matter what it is made of – brass, copper or wood. Watt wrestled with this problem for over a year without making any progress, but while he was out walking one day in May 1765 the solution came to him in a sudden flash of inspiration. The way to escape from this apparently impossible dilemma was to use TWO cylinders; one of them could be kept hot all the time, but it would be connected to a second cylinder which was kept cool. The power would be produced by the piston moving in the hot cylinder, but at each stroke a valve would be opened and the steam could be condensed in the cold cylinder by a jet of cold water. Watt set about building a model and was convinced that his simple but brilliant idea could lead to a much more efficient and economical type of engine. But, as Papin had found

earlier, there was to be a long struggle ahead to convert the ideas into practice.

THE YEARS OF FAILURE

The next few years were to be the lowest point in Watt's life. He started with great enthusiasm, and gave up his work for the university, moving into a larger workshop so as to concentrate on building engines. He soon ran into serious problems though, and his money gradually drained away. Joseph Black helped as much as he could and Watt supported himself by doing other work, such as surveying for the construction of the Caledonian canal.

It seemed that his fortunes had changed when Black introduced him to Roebuck, a mine owner, who was prepared to finance the production of engines to pump water from his coal mines. But even with Watt's great mechanical skills, the inferior machine tools and materials that were available in Glasgow made it almost impossible to produce cylinders and pistons which were both steam-tight and free moving.

In 1767 he visited Birmingham and met Erasmus Darwin and William Small, two of the founders of the Lunar Society. They were both enthusiastic about the

Watt and Boulton's Rotative Beam pumping engine of 1797.

potential of Watt's ideas, and they told Matthew Boulton, one of the great industrialists of the time, about Watt's plans and his problems in developing them. In 1768 Boulton tried to arrange for the transfer of the patent in order to take over the development, but Roebuck was unwilling to give up while there still

seemed to be any hope of success.

But there was little real progress over the next few years. The engines were still very unreliable, and when they broke down the mines flooded. Eventually in 1773 Roebuck went bankrupt and their partnership came to an end. In the same year Watt suffered a terrible personal blow when his wife died, leaving him to look after their two young children.

After nine years of hard work Watt seemed to have been defeated.

WATT AND BOULTON

The turning point came in 1774 when Matthew Boulton offered him a new partnership. At that time the facilities in Birmingham were far superior to anything that were available in Scotland, and Watt moved all that could be salvaged to Boulton's workshops. With the new facilities, and the encouragement of his new partner, he set to work again. In 1775 they were granted a twenty five year extension of Watt's patent and by the next year the first fully successful engine was installed to drive the air pump for a blast furnace. In this year Watt married his second wife, Ann McGregor.

Matthew Boulton had inherited his father's buckle making business in 1759 and his energy soon brought expansion into a new factory and diversification into many other areas of metal working. He was another member of the Lunar society and had first become interested in the possibilities of the steam engine even before he heard of James Watt's ideas. He proved to be the ideal partner for Watt. Not only did he provide finance, well equipped workshops and commercial skills, but they also complemented each other's personalities. Watt's inclination to be cautious and pessimistic was balanced by Boulton's enthusiasm and optimism for their great new joint venture. When James Boswell visited the factory in 1776 Boulton told him: "I sell here, sir, what all the world desires to have – power."

There were, however, still several more years of development work ahead and the company did not begin to make a profit until the 1780s, but gradually Boulton and Watt established a solid reputation for producing engines which were not only reliable but also far more powerful and more economical than any produced before. Their engines were increasingly widely installed all over the country, especially in coal and tin mines.

THE BEGINNING OF THE STEAM AGE

Watt had many ideas for further developments, but at first he was fully occupied in overseeing the production of the engines and supervising their installation. Boulton, however, could see that there was still an immense untapped market for steam power to drive the machinery in factories and textile mills; but this required a different type of engine. Until then the only way to produce rotary action was cumbersome and inefficient: an engine was used to pump water which then drove a water wheel. Eventually Boulton persuaded Watt to develop his design for an engine which could drive a rotating shaft directly, and over the next ten years he produced many other important refinements, including the double action engine, and the governor to control the speed of a flywheel. By the 1790s the steam engine was, in all essentials, fully developed.

Watt took a prominent part in the activities of the Lunar Society, which played such an important role during these years in bringing together scientists and the new industrialists. His earlier interest in chemistry, which had developed through his friendship with Joseph Black, was renewed when he met Priestley. He carried out some investigations into the nature of water and also devised a chemical method for copying documents, which remained a standard office technique for many years. More closely related to his main work, he saw that there was a need for some means of comparing the output of different engines and he developed the scientific idea of work, introducing a unit for measuring power output, horsepower. It is very appropriate that the later international scientific unit for the measurement of power, the watt, was named after him. He was elected as a Fellow of the Royal Society in 1785.

During the 1790s Boulton and Watt increasingly brought their sons into the business and in 1794 set up the firm Boulton, Watt and Sons. Their engines were now essential to industry not only in Britain, but were also being exported to the Continent and to North America. By now both Boulton and Watt had become wealthy men. Watt continued working on refinements of the engine and on other inventions until the end of his life, although by 1800 he had retired from active participation in the company.

When he died in 1819 at the age of eighty three, the age of steam was already well launched: his great partnership with Matthew Boulton had literally powered the Industrial Revolution. His achievements were marked by a memorial in Westminster Abbey which describes him as a benefactor of humanity who increased the powers of man.

CHAPTER XIV

(1781 – 1848) & (1803 – 1859)
GEORGE &
ROBERT STEPHENSON

George Stephenson was born in the village of Wylam, 9 miles from Newcastle-upon-Tyne. His father, another Robert, was a fireman, whose job was to shovel coal for one of the steam pumping engines at the local colliery. This village and its colliery have a special place in the history of railways. Not only was it the birthplace of the man who has been called "The Father of Railways", it was also to be the place where the first successful steam railway was operated by another pioneer, William Hedley, in 1814.

TRAVEL IN THE NINETEENTH CENTURY

The world into which George was born was very different from ours in many ways, but one of the most striking was the absence of any means of cheap and speedy transport. Most people never went much further from the place they were born than to the nearest towns and if they needed to travel, unless they were wealthy they had to walk. For example, if George's father had wanted to go to London even the fastest coaches would have taken about four days – and the fare would have been the equivalent of his year's wages. Improvements to the roads in the late eighteenth century by men like McAdam made travel a little easier, but it was the coming of the railways in the 1830's that transformed not only commerce and the distribution of food, but eventually the whole social structure, by providing transport which was for the first time within the means of ordinary people.

George Stephenson's title "father of the railways", which was first used during his lifetime, is well deserved, although he invented neither the locomotive nor idea of a railway track. The basic idea of a railway had originated three hundred years earlier, when miners in sixteenth century Europe found it much easier to push a truck through underground chambers on parallel wooden planks than to push it through the mud.

A COLLIERY CHILDHOOD

George Stephenson was introduced to this type of primitive railway at an early age. His family was too poor for him to go to school and he started work at the age of eight – being paid a shilling a week to keep cattle from straying onto the colliery "plateway", which passed close to the cottage in which he was born. This was a wooden track along which horse drawn carts transported coal to the Tyne, where it was loaded into barges or keels.

By the age of eighteen George had already begun to show his mechanical skill and was put in charge of one of the winding engines at the colliery. He was fascinated by machinery and often stayed on after working hours to take an engine apart and rebuild it. Like his whole family he was at this time still almost completely illiterate, but he resolved to educate himself and began to attend evening classes. By the time he was married three years later, he was able to sign his own name in the marriage register, even though in an unformed hand.

Stephenson's new locomotive pulling a ceremonial train of open-air coal and passenger waggons along the Stockton to Darlington railway.

ROBERT STEPHENSON

The couple moved to Willington, where he was to take charge of a new winding engine, and it was here that his son Robert was born in October 1803. At Willington Colliery something new was being tried: a steam engine was being used to pull the coal wagons up the steeper parts of the track by cable, although horses were still used for the main part of the haulage.

In 1804 they moved again, to Killingworth, north of Newcastle, and here their second child, Fanny, was born. But it was a difficult birth and the little girl died after only three weeks. His wife's health had also been weakened and she never fully recovered. She died in the following year, leaving George a widower of twenty five to look after their only surviving child, Robert, with the help of his unmarried sister, Nelly.

His depression increased still further when his father was badly injured in a colliery accident and for some time he seriously considered emigrating. But eventually he found new purpose by taking charge of the education of his son. Throughout his life, George remained very sensitive about his own lack of education and, at least partly in compensation, he was determined that Robert would have the advantages that he had missed. He was by now relatively well paid, through promotions resulting from his increasing abilities as an engineer, and he was able to afford the fees for Robert to attend a private school in Newcastle. He also bought him a pony for the daily five mile journey to school with all his books. He worked with his son, helping him and learning with him, and when Robert went on from school to the Newcastle Literary and Philosophical Society, George felt sufficiently confident to join too. But although he was later to become a national, indeed

Robert Stephenson in 1858 beside hydraulic lifting equipment used for constructing the railways.

an international figure, he rarely wrote his own letters and always felt diffident about speaking in public because of his broad "Geordie" accent.

He worked on many inventions, often assisted by Robert, and was able to supplement his income by designing improved colliery engines for pumping and winding. In 1815 he invented a miner's safety lamp, but this brought him into controversy with the great Sir Humphrey Davy, who until his death was unable to believe that an unknown and uneducated man like

Stephenson could have hit upon the same idea as himself independently without cheating. Nevertheless, he was something of a hero in the North, not least for standing his ground. A public subscription was organised and enough was collected for Stephenson to be awarded £1000 in gratitude for his invention.

TREVITHICK'S ENGINE

In 1805 the Cornish mechanic Richard Trevithick visited Tyneside (and it is said that he met George and

his infant son during this visit). Trevithick had already been experimenting with mobile steam engines – locomotives – for some years. His first, in 1801, was a road vehicle, but this was a short lived experiment. On one of its first outings it went out of control while going along a bumpy road at Cambourne in Cornwall. The locomotive crashed into a house and was damaged beyond repair. In 1804 he built a much more successful engine, this time designed to run on a railway track. In a demonstration it hauled ten tons of steel and seventy men. This was an historic event, which could be claimed as the birth of the railway, but it proved to be a dead end. The locomotive was too heavy for the wooden tracks that were being used and the experiment was reluctantly abandoned.

Following Trevithick's visit to Tyneside a locomotive was built in Gateshead, but it was never used because Trevithick had still not overcome the problems of a heavy locomotive breaking up the wooden plateway. Nevertheless, the idea had taken root by now and over the next few years many others began to experiment. In 1813 the wooden track at Wylam colliery was replaced by iron rails and it was there, in Stephenson's birthplace, that the first fully successful locomotive was built by William Hedley. One of its successors, "Puffing Billy" of 1827, the world's oldest surviving locomotive, can be seen in the Science Museum in London.

THE LOCOMOTION

George Stephenson was one unknown, if unusually gifted, colliery mechanic among many when he built his first engine, "Locomotion". This ran for the first time in July 1814 with his brother James at the controls. Like most early locomotives it was not very reliable at first, but Stephenson constantly worked on it, thinking of improvements both to the engine and the track. In one important innovation he hit upon the idea of directing a blast of exhaust steam up the chimney to increase the draft and was therefore able to develop greater power. His reputation began to spread, although railways did not attract much attention beyond the collieries until a far-sighted pamphlet was written by Thomas Grey in 1820. He was the first to propose the building of a network of railways to connect all the major cities of Britain. He claimed that this would "revolutionise the face of the world" and he also made detailed calculations

to show that, once established, the system could greatly reduce the cost of travel and would soon pay for the great cost of its construction.

THE STOCKTON TO DARLINGTON RAILWAY

Others, too, now began to become excited by the commercial possibilities of the idea, and it was Edward Pease who first gave Stephenson the possibility of moving on to a larger stage. Pease was one of a group of Quaker merchants in Darlington; he had become convinced that a railway would provide a more efficient link between Stockton and Darlington than the canal which was at that time being planned. He gathered a group of businessmen together, mainly fellow Quakers, raised the finance and single-mindedly pushed the idea along until at last in 1821 he achieved his goal of getting permission, through an act of Parliament, to build a public railway. At this time it was intended to be a horse-drawn tramway – the existing colliery locomotives did not seem to offer serious competition, even in speed. But in the April of that year Pease decided to investigate the possibility of using steam locomotives and met Stephenson for the first time. He was soon enthusiastic about the idea and, once he had overcome the doubts of some of the other directors, Stephenson was commissioned to survey the line.

They were creating something entirely new, and over the next four years Stephenson set many of the patterns which are still followed today. For example one of his first decisions was that the gauge (the distance between the two rails) should be 4ft 8½ inches. Nobody seems to be quite sure why he hit upon this rather odd figure. The later engineer Brunel used a six foot gauge when he built the Great Western Railway and tried hard to get this accepted as the standard. But eventually this had to be rebuilt to Stephenson's gauge, and 4ft 8½ inches is still the standard for railways in many countries throughout the world.

The first rail of the world's first public railway was laid in Stockton in May 1822. There was an impressive ceremony, with a procession through the town accompanied by the pealing of church bells. Prominent in the procession were 300 workmen who were to build the track; these were the first of the railway "navvies", who were to march as a great army throughout the length and

The three serious contenders for the historic Rainhill trial of 8th October 1829: the Stephensons' Rocket (top), and Northumbrian (bottom), and Braithwaite and Ericsson's Novelty (centre).

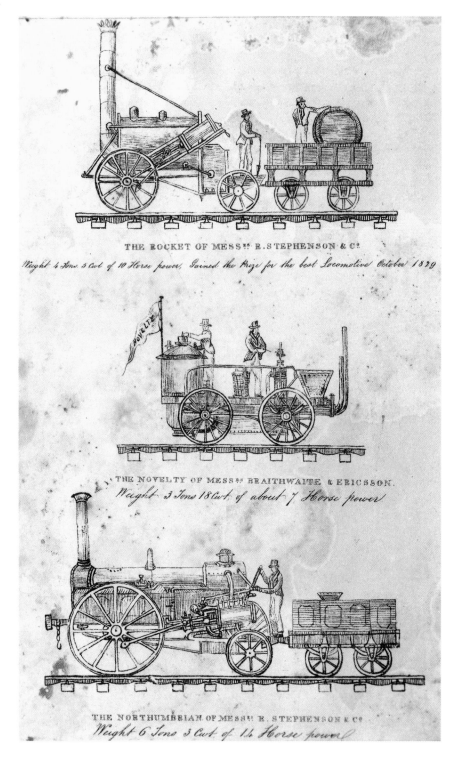

THE ROCKET OF MESS.ᴿˢ R.STEPHENSON & Cᵒ.

Weight 4 Tons 5 Cwt of 10 Horse power, Gained the Prize for the best Locomotive October 1829

THE NOVELTY OF MESS.ᴿˢ BRAITHWAITE & ERICSSON.

Weight 3 Tons 18 Cwt of about 7 Horse power

THE NORTHUMBRIAN OF MESS.ᴿˢ R. STEPHENSON & Cᵒ.

Weight 6 Tons 3 Cwt of 14 Horse power

breadth of Britain over the next forty years. Three years later, on September 27th 1825, the Stockton to Darlington Railway was officially opened. Great crowds of spectators had come from miles around, many arriving at dawn for a good vantage point to see the "iron horse". Eventually "Locomotion" set off with George at the controls, hauling a specially built carriage for the directors and other main guests – followed by thirty other wagons which carried over five hundred other passengers. But one important person who missed this historic occasion was his son, Robert, who was away on a visit to South America.

THE ROCKET

This was a historic milestone, and was recognised at the time as something very important and exciting, although Stockton and Darlington were not, themselves, towns of outstanding importance. But a much larger project was being planned: a railway to connect two of the rapidly growing industrial centres, Liverpool and Manchester. At first many of the directors of this venture thought that fixed engines – hauling wagons by means of cables – would be more reliable than the still relatively untried lococomotives. It was decided to hold a trial and to award a prize of £500 if a locomotive could be produced to meet their requirements. George Stephenson was already fully occupied working the construction the track, so his son Robert was entrusted with building their entry for the competition, "The Rocket". On the first day of the famous Rainhill Trial, 8th October 1829, only four of the original ten entrants were ready (and one of the four was not really a serious contender, being powered by a horse). It was organised almost like a race meeting and each competitor had to complete a course of sixty miles. George took the controls of the "Rocket" – and on some occasions, during the two weeks of the trials, he opened up the throttle to reach the terrifying and unprecedented speed of over 50 kilometres per hour.

Although his locomotive may look very primitive

Robert Stephenson's Britannia tubular iron-work bridge in Wales.

Stephenson's world-famous Rocket, donated to the Patent Office Museum in 1862.

today, surrounded by later locomotives in the Science Museum in London, it was far ahead of its competitors and won the trial easily, despite considerable opposition from some of the London-based experts. It had finally proved that railways could be a reliable, safe – and above all an economical – means of transport. For Robert it lead to an immediate order for another four locomotives, to be built by Robert Stephenson and Company. From the beginning this would be a busy line, unlike the one locomotive used on the Stockton to Darlington line. George had to invent for the first time methods of signalling, the idea of railway timetabling and many of the procedures which were to become a routine part of running a railway safely and efficiently.

THE RAILWAY AGE BEGINS

The opening ceremony was a great national event attended, among many thousands of others by the Prime Minister, the Duke of Wellington, and by other prominent statesmen including Sir Robert Peel and Lord Grey, who were both to become prime ministers. The day was unfortunately marred by the first fatal railway accident. When the train which was carrying Wellington stopped to take on water, several of the passengers got out, including William Huskisson, a prominent member of parliament. Huskisson walked along the track to the Duke's carriage and while they were talking the "Rocket", with Stephenson at the controls, approached along the other track. The more agile passengers managed to jump clear but Huskisson was run over and died a few hours later. After a delay and anxious discussions, it was decided that the ceremonies should continue. Despite the tragedy the day marked a historic turning point: with the completion of the Manchester to Liverpool line the era of mass transport had arrived.

In its first full year of operation the line carried half a million passengers and it was soon having an impact on other aspects of life, providing cheap and rapid transport of fresh food to the industrial areas. With remarkable speed railways also began to spread throughout the world. Observers from America had attended the Rainhill Trial and the first railways in France and America were built in 1830. With its vast distances and scattered population the railway was to play an essential part in opening up the west and in drawing America together.

In many countries during the next few years hundreds of fortunes would be made and lost and thousands of workmen would give their lives during the rush to build rival railways. The Stephensons, who in 1836 moved the headquarters of their company to London, were at the centre of this "railway mania", as it has been called. But many other engineers were also beginning to come to prominence. In 1833 Robert Stephenson was appointed as Chief Engineer to the London to Birmingham Railway and another young man, Isambard Kingdom Brunel, who was also under thirty, took up a similar post with the projected Great Western Railway. There was to be much rivalry between the two men over the next twenty years.

THE DEATH OF GEORGE STEPHENSON

By 1844 the new age had provided the inspiration for one of J.M.W. Turner's late paintings: "Rail, Steam and Speed". George was by this time a rich man, who had played an important part in the building of railways, not only in Britain but in many other countries of Europe. One of his last major ventures, at the age of sixty four, was to carry out a survey for a railway from Madrid to the coast. His exertions brought on an attack of pleurisy from which he only just recovered. When he returned to England he gradually retired from all active work and spent his last years living simply, raising chickens and growing fruit. In August 1848 the pleurisy recurred and he died on 12th August, at the age of sixty seven. He was buried in Chesterfield but, for someone who had been so famous in his lifetime it was a rather unimpressive ceremony, attended by none of the great men of the day, apart from Robert. One of the few important people from his early days who did attend was Edward Pease, now over eighty.

ENGINEERING FOR THE RAILWAYS

Among George Stephenson's greatest ambitions had been to give his son the education he had lacked; thanks to this, Robert went on to become one of the greatest engineers of the Victorian age. Unlike his father, who remained to the end a rather gruff "self-made man", Robert was accepted by, and felt at home with, the London establishment. He is famed for his bridges as much as for his contribution to setting up the railway system. One of his greatest monuments is the High Level bridge over the Tyne at Newcastle, which was opened by Queen Victoria in 1849. Together with his bridge over the river Tweed at Berwick, this completed the rail link between London and Edinburgh. He travelled all over the world; he built a bridge over the Nile, and one of his greatest structures is the bridge over the St. Lawrence River at Montreal in Canada.

In 1847 he became Member of Parliament for Whitby, one of the many public offices and honours that were bestowed on him, although he refused the offer of a knighthood. He had always worked long hours and when his wife died in 1842 he drove himself even harder, taking little care for his health.

Robert Stephenson died in September 1859 at the early age of fifty six, in the same month as his rival the other great railway engineer, Isambard Kingdom Brunel. In contrast with his father's rather humble funeral eleven years earlier, he was buried in Westminster Abbey with an impressive ceremony which was attended by more than three thousand mourners, including many of the greatest names of the day from the worlds of politics, science and engineering.

In our century the car and the plane were to make their own great impact on transport, but the truly revolutionary change had already taken place. With the coming of the railways, the world had become smaller. As William Thackeray wrote:

"We who have lived before the railways were made belong to a different world".

CHAPTER XV

(1847 – 1922)
ALEXANDER GRAHAM BELL

Before the Industrial Revolution the pace of life was slower and the world a larger place. News, like passengers, travelled no faster than the speed of a horse, or via fire beacons from hill-top to hill top if it was important enough. Parallel to the changes which took place in the transport of people and materials, the creation of our modern world also depended upon (and in its turn produced) a vast increase in the flow of information. Today commerce and industry rely upon the ability to make contact with customers or suppliers rapidly wherever they are, and we have come to accept the same facility for keeping in touch with our friends and families, or for calling help in an emergency. There are now over six hundred million telephones, part of a web of communications that can put us in contact with almost anybody on earth at the touch of a few buttons. The telephone has been part of everyday life for most of the twentieth century; this now essential part of our world began with the first telephone message by Alexander Graham Bell in 1876.

NEWS FROM AFAR

Communicating at a distance was not a new idea. The use of beacons is mentioned in the Old Testament, and the Romans elaborated this idea into chains of signalling stations which could pass on the warning of an attack. Similar systems were set up in the fifteenth century by the Scottish parliament to warn against raids by the English (one bonfire indicated a small attack, and up to four fires gave warning of a major incursion).

When the semaphore was invented in the late eighteenth century it became possible for the first time to send quite detailed information rapidly over great distances. For example in 1795 Napoleon Bonaparte received intelligence reports and sent his orders to the armies on the French borders by this means. In England at about the same time a chain of semaphore stations was set up between London and Portsmouth in order to pass on the exact time from Greenwich Observatory (this was required by the navy for accurate navigation). But systems of this type were limited in potential, being very

Professor Alexander Graham Bell inaugurating the New York to Chicago telephone line with due ceremony in October 1892.

THIS MODEL OF BELL'S FIRST TELEPHONE IS A DUPLICATE OF THE INSTRUMENT THROUGH WHICH SPEECH SOUNDS WERE FIRST TRANSMITTED ELECTRICALLY, 1875.

dependant on the weather conditions and on the accuracy of human observers as they watched through telescopes for the distant signal and then passed the message along the chain.

The first really major advance in communications came in the mid nineteenth century with the invention of the electric telegraph. There were several earlier experiments which successfully transmitted simple messages along wires for distances of a few miles, but an American, Joseph Henry (1797 – 1878), is generally credited with developing the first practical telegraph system in 1831. This was also one of the earliest practical fruits of the work of Faraday and others on electromagnetism (see Chapter V). But all that could be transmitted by the telegraph were pulses of electricity – dots and dashes – and there had to be some general agreement on how these should be used to convey information.

MORSE CODE
Samuel Morse (1791 – 1851) exhibited his code for the first time to the United States Congress in 1837, and this soon became the standard throughout the world. In 1845 the first telegraph company was set up to connect New York and Washington, and a printing telegraph was demonstrated in 1854. The telegraph spread rapidly, and by 1866, after five previous attempts, a link between Britain and America was established by means of a submarine cable which was laid by Isambard Kingdom Brunel's steam ship "Great Eastern" – at that time the world's largest ship. Before the end of the century cables had been installed under the Pacific ocean, and most of the major cities of the world had been linked together.

THE TELEGRAPHY OF THE VOICE
It occurred to several people that the idea of telegraphy might be taken a stage further, so as to transmit not just messages but the human voice itself. This was a much more complicated undertaking, though. Instead of simple on/off electrical impulses, the dots and dashes of the Morse code, it would be necessary to transmit enough of the timbre of the sound for it to be recognisable as a human voice; and if it was to be a practical communications system, the sound had to be loud and clear enough for the words to be understood even after passing along hundreds of miles of wire.

One of the first experiments in telephony was carried out in 1860, by Philipp Reis in Germany. He was able to transmit sounds of a fixed pitch along a wire, but he did not develop the idea much further. The decisive step was taken twelve years later, almost simultaneously by Elisha Gray (1835-1901) and Alexander Graham Bell, both working in the United States.

It has been said that if Bell had known much about electricity at the time he started his work he would have decided that it was impossible and would never have invented the telephone. He was far from being a "self taught genius", like Stephenson or Edison, but his main knowledge and interest had been in the field of sound rather than electricity. In fact there had been a family history of important work on sound and speech.

THREE GENERATIONS
His grandfather was an authority on elocution and his father, Alexander Melville Bell, had followed in his footsteps. At the time of Alexander Graham's birth in 1847 the family lived in Edinburgh. After studying at Edinburgh University he taught for a while and then

An advertisement of the 1880's showing the exciting uses of the new telephone apparatus throughout the U.S.A.

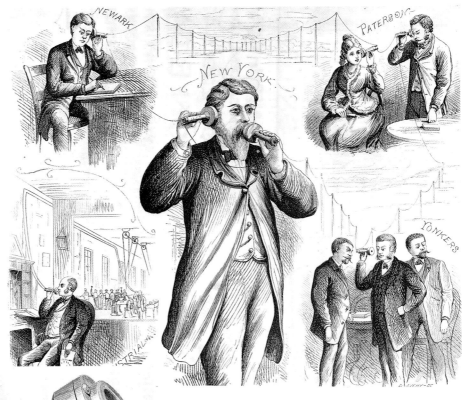

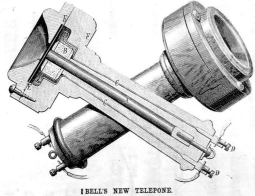

BELL'S NEW TELEPONE.

went to London to study medicine at University College. He went on to take a Ph.D. degree at Würtzburg after two years of research on sound waves.

Bell's father moved to London in 1865 where he published his work on "Visible Speech". This summed up the twenty years of work he had carried out to establish a system of phonetics, which he had also developed into an aid for teaching the deaf to speak. In 1868 he toured the United States to lecture on this phonetic system, and he found such interest in his work that in 1870 he decided to emigrate there and settled in Washington. After Alexander Graham had completed his education he joined the rest of the family in America and also began to devote himself to the teaching of the deaf and dumb, and to spreading his father's system of phonetics. He set up the Boston Training School for the Deaf and from 1873 to 1877 he was professor of Vocal Physiology at Boston university. In 1874 he became a naturalised citizen of the United States.

THE IDEA

By the early 1870s the electric telegraph had already become so firmly established that its use was beginning to outstrip the number of lines available. The installation of thousands of miles of additional wires was very expensive so there was a search for ways of increasing the efficiency of the existing lines. Resulting from his knowledge of sound, Bell was sponsored to work on a possible means of increasing capacity by what was called a "harmonic" telegraph system. By this he tried to send more than one message along a telegraph line by using different tones, so that a high-pitched tone would carry one message, a lower-pitched tone a different message and a lower pitch again yet another message. By tuning some reeds at both ends more than one message could be sent down the line at the same time. From this work he realised that if he could send tones, perhaps he could also send speech, which is, of course, a combination of tones.

Bell explained this hope to his assistant, Thomas Watson (1854-1934): "If I could make an electric current vary in intensity, precisely as the air varies in density when a sound passes through it, I should be able to transmit any sound telegraphically, even the sound of speech".

A CHANCE DISCOVERY

Bell and Watson continued their work on the telegraph system but in 1875 they made an important discovery. They had set up a circuit to send electric pulses between two rooms, and were using three thin strips of steel at each end to act as tuned receivers so as to disentangle the three messages. One of the steel reeds at Watson's end was not working properly and as he prodded at it, making a twanging noise, Bell noticed that the receiver in his room was making a faint twanging noise in response. He realised that this was because the steel strips had become slightly magnetised, and when the one at Watson's end vibrated it must be creating a fluctuating electric current. This was transmitted along the wire and, in turn, caused the steel strip in Bell's room to vibrate and so re-create the twanging sound.

This fortunate chance observation gave him the variable current he had talked about and he realised that all the main essentials for transmitting sound were there. Bell and Watson knew they were close to their goal, but there was still a lot of work to be done before the idea could be developed into a practical means of conveying recognisable speech. There were many possible variations of the equipment – different tensions of the springs, different strengths of the magnets, different types of coil, different materials to be tried, and so on. They worked long hours, mainly in the attic of his house in Boston, until eventually they succeeded in finding the right combination. According to the most common story, Bell spilled some acid on himself and called out: "Come here Mr. Watson, I want to see you". Watson was in the other room and heard this message coming over their circuit. He rushed through, shouting: "I can hear you – perfect – wonderful"! The world's first telephone conversation had taken place.

ELISHA GRAY

Meanwhile, in Chicago Elisha Gray had been working on a similar idea, but using a rather more cumbersome apparatus. On 14th February 1876 he lodged a preliminary application with the United States patent office – but on the same day, just a few hours earlier, Bell had already submitted a full specification of his system together with diagrams, and it was his system which was granted the patent. He had soon developed his invention to the point where he could demonstrate it to others, and these became dramatic occasions attracting large audiences. Bell arranged for people to sing, play trumpets and recite Shakespeare down the telephone line and, even with this very early equipment, the results

An early telephone switchboard made in Cincinatti in 1879, designed for fifty subscribers. It was one of the first switchboards installed by the Bell Telephone Company in Norway.

were clear enough for the words to be heard and understood. From the beginning there was great interest and enthusiasm for something which was recognised to be not just a scientific curiosity but a most important advance in communication.

The Bell Telephone Company was founded in 1877 and, with the help of Watson, the quality and range of the equipment was steadily improved. The telephone spread with remarkable speed; for example, within two years of the original invention a telephone system was installed in Marlborough House, the residence of the Prince of Wales. Clearly it was something the world had been waiting for. But to become a practical means of communication it was necessary to devise ways of connecting the large number of potential users. This problem was solved in 1878, when the first telephone exchange was opened at New Haven, Conneticut. A similar exchange was set up the following year in London and soon trunk lines began to spread out to connect the major towns in many countries. By 1891 Paris and London had been linked by a cross-channel cable.

There were to be many disputes over priority; several inventors had been working independently on the general idea of the telephone, and on the various component parts of the equipment. Legal battles over Bell's patent continued for more than twenty years, but in the end he won all the major disputes and is today generally accepted as the sole inventor of the telephone.

NEW INVENTIONS

Bell's greatest invention was, in all essentials, completed while he was still in his early thirties, but he turned his inventive mind to many other areas during his seventy five years. He became interested in genetics and did some sheep breeding. He designed kites and for some time worked at the idea of producing a powered version. As a spin-off from his interest in aeronautics he produced a hydrofoil boat which held the world speed record for many years. He devised a way of transmitting sound without wires which he called a Photophone, using a light beam. He also produced a gramophone very similar to Edison's phonograph and introduced the wax cylinder which helped to spread the phonograph as a popular means of home entertainment (see Chapter XVI). He also founded the journal *Science*.

The telephone has gone through many changes since

its early days. The instrument itself has gradually evolved over the years in appearance and in sophistication, although we still hark back to earlier days when we talk of "giving a ring" or "hanging up". There have also been great changes in the means of linking lines together. The early telephone exchanges, with banks of plugs and sockets connected by human operators, have gradually been replaced by increasingly efficient and complex automatic dialling. (The first automatic exchange was opened as early as 1892 in Indiana). The original wires and cables linking callers have been supplemented by the use of microwave radio, and most cities have their equivalent of London's Post Office Tower, which provides thousands of telephone circuits connecting with all parts of the country. More recently satellites have taken over from submarine cables as the main means of intercontinental communication, but in the near future even these will be insufficient for the increasing flow of one of our world's most valuable commodities: information. The most recent developments return to Bell's idea of transmitting sound by light rays, but in a far more sophisticated form using laser beams travelling along bundles of thin glass fibres. These can carry far more messages with a much lower degree of distortion than can be achieved by using electric currents, and so a new generation of cables, using fibre optics, is beginning to spread around the world.

THE BEL

Bell's interest in sound was the common thread running through his most important work. It is therefore very fitting that the scientific unit for measuring the intensity of sound was later named after him. The unit itself (the bel) is rather large and we are more familiar with tenths of this unit, or decibels.

The vast extent to which the world's communications system would grow, and even the nature of much of the information carried today, would have been far beyond even Bell's fertile imagination at the time of his first telephone message. Today fax machines transmitting copies of documents, and computers in direct contact with other computers, share this network with people talking to their family or friends, whether in the next street or on opposite sides of the world. Alexander Graham Bell's invention rapidly became one of the most indispensable features of our world.

CHAPTER XVI

(1847 – 1931)
THOMAS ALVAR EDISON

Thomas Edison followed the same tradition as James Watt and George Stephenson, as a self-made man. He had little formal education, but he went on to make a fortune – and to change the world. In the late nineteenth century it was still possible for one man with bright ideas to work on his own. Although he started in this way, Edison himself was largely responsible for bringing the era of the solitary inventor to an end. He is most remembered for inventing the phonograph and electric lighting, but he also invented a new way of organising the development and exploitation of such inventions.

THE YOUNG BUSINESSMAN

Edison's father had moved from Canada to the United States in 1837 after coming into conflict with the government. His son Thomas was born in Milan, Ohio, in 1847. He received a very basic education from his mother, who had been a teacher, but he had little aptitude for formal study. Thomas was very poor at

mathematics, although he showed an early interest in science. At the age of ten he began working and spent much of his time selling newspapers and vegetables. By the time he was twelve, Edison was employing other boys to help him, and soon gained the exclusive right to sell papers on the railway line running into Detroit. Later he bought some old printing equipment and with the help of four assistants for a time he produced his own paper, "The Grand Trunk Herald".

THE FIRST INVENTIONS

In his teens he had become interested in telegraphy, and an opportunity to train as an operator came when a stationmaster offered to teach him as a reward when Edison saved his son from an oncoming train. He soon became a skilled operator – and was later to nickname his first two children Dot and Dash, after the Morse code. It was the practical experience gained in these years which turned his inventive mind towards electricity. By chance he obtained a copy of the works of Michael Faraday

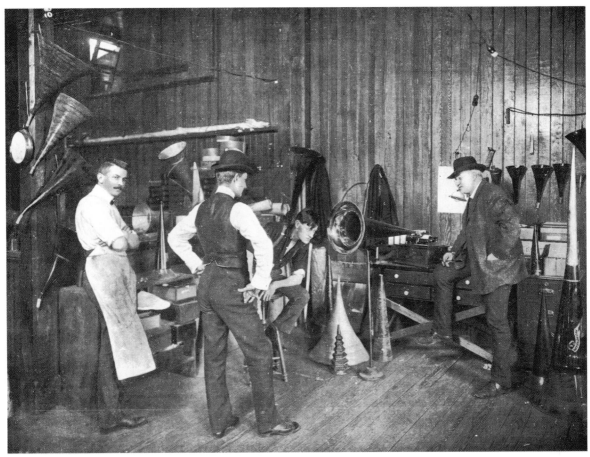

Edison testing the latest model of phonograph in his workshop in the early 1890's.

(chapter V), and this gave him some scientific foundation for the knowledge that he was picking up. He also began making and patenting inventions, at first mainly small technical improvements to the telegraph system.

One invention from this period was to be very important later. This was an automatic repeater which could record a telegraph message and re-transmit it on another line without another operator having to be present. The device included a cylinder which was rotated by a clockwork motor, and the series of dots and dashes from the telegraph message were impressed on it in their correct sequence as the recording head moved along the cylinder. When it was recording a high speed message Edison noticed that the sound of the rattling lever took on a musical tone, and this was later to give him the basic idea for a much more important invention.

By the time he was twenty-one he had gained sufficient experience and confidence to launch into his third career, as a professional inventor. One of his first projects was an electrical vote recorder which he hoped would be taken up by the U.S. Congress. But they showed no interest and it proved to be a complete flop. It was nevertheless a valuable lesson for Edison: however good the idea may be in itself, he also had to be sure it would find a market.

EDISON IN NEW YORK

Later in the same year, 1872, he moved to New York. He arrived with very little money, but within a week he joined with a friend to set up in business as "Electrical Engineers" – one of the first uses of this term. He became involved with operating the "ticker tape" equipment of the New York Stock Exchange and soon began to devise many improvements, including a printing telegraph for transmitting stockmarket prices. He eventually held forty-six patents in this field. The original business was sold at a profit and he invested his proceeds to set up a new business in a workshop at Newark, New Jersey. Before long he was employing fifty people who were engaged in the development and manufacture of various kinds of telegraphic equipment. This was the forerunner of the famous Menlo Park workshop, the purpose-built laboratories into which he moved when he needed to expand the business.

Over the next few years Edison threw himself into his work with great energy, at times working on more than forty different developments simultaneously. The two inventions for which he is most famous, the phonograph and the electric lamp, were products of this "inventions factory".

THE PHONOGRAPH

Of all his inventions the phonograph, dating from 1877, was Edison's own favourite. The mechanism was based on his earlier apparatus for recording telegraph messages, and the person who wished to record a message spoke into a conical funnel which focussed the sound onto a diaphragm. This was connected to a sharp steel stylus which was made to vibrate by the diaphragm and so cut a groove in a piece of tin foil which was wrapped round the cylinder. In this simple way the changes in air pressure that make up the sound waves were converted to a groove of varying depth. The stylus was then rewound to its original position, but now when the cylinder was rotated the stylus moved up and down in the groove which had been made previously. In turn this caused the diaphragm to vibrate, so re-creating the original sound.

Edison himself was partly deaf and not very interested in music. He originally thought the main application of the phonograph would be as a dictating machine for use in offices. Hundreds were manufactured and sold for this purpose, but it was soon evident that it had even greater potential as an new form of home entertainment. Alexander Graham Bell (Chapter XV), who also worked on a similar invention, introduced the use of wax cylinders to replace Edison's original tin foil. Although these were rather fragile they allowed a more faithful copy of the sound to be made. Despite their limited

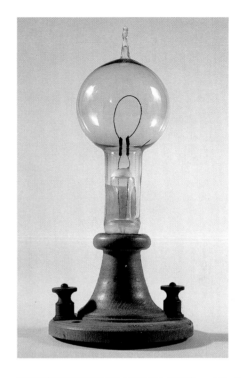

The Edison light bulb using the innovative platinum filament.

Edison's dynamo based on the Warner Siemens design, and set up in the first electrical power station in New York in 1881.

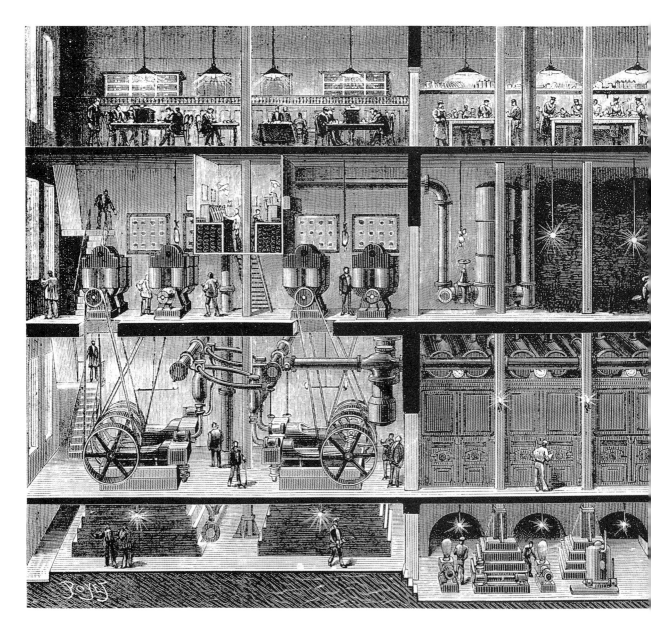

quality of reproduction these early records created a great popular impact. Recordings made by famous artists, most notably the great tenor Enrico Caruso, helped to establish the phonograph as much more than a novelty.

THE GRAMAPHONE

Since the time of Edison there have been many further developments which have gradually transformed the quality of sound reproduction. In many ways the gramophone patented by Emile Berliner in 1887 is the more direct ancestor of later record players. This used a flat disc instead of a cylinder and the disc eventually won the initial battle between the two systems. By the 1930s the quality of reproduction was greatly increased by using electrical methods both to record and to amplify the sound. Further progress came when microgroove long-

The Edison power station in Pearl Street supplying New York with electrical power from the 1880's.

as it moves along a groove. Nevertheless he was the first to demonstrate the possibility of recording sound, and to build this idea into an international industry. Many early phonograph recordings can still be heard and some have even been transferred to their distant descendant, the compact disc.

THE ELECTRIC LIGHT

The other great invention to come from Edison's Menlo Park workshop was the development of the electric lamp. This was not an original idea and one form of electric lighting, the arc lamp, had already been in use for several years. But this was only suitable where intense light was required, for example for street lights or in large open spaces such as railway stations. A new form of electric light, suitable for domestic use, was needed. A patent had been taken out for a platinum filament lamp by the American J.W. Starr as early as 1845, and Joseph Swan (1828-1917) in England was to begin his first experiments a few years later.

The main problems at this time were to find a material for the filament which was capable of withstanding the high temperature, and also to find ways of excluding air from the bulb so that the white hot filament would not burn up.

Swan demonstrated his first successful carbon filament lamp to the Chemical Society at Newcastle upon Tyne in December 1878 and took out patents in Britain. Edison was working along very similar lines and his research team had investigated thousands of alternative materials before hitting upon a very similar product. There was a legal battle between the two men for several years but in 1883 they eventually resolved their differences and joined forces, in the Edison and Swan Electric Light Company, to develop and exploit their joint invention, the "Ediswan" lamp.

THE FIRST POWER STATIONS

But Edison went much further than this. A lamp was not much use without an electricity supply and a power station to generate it. Taking the idea a logical step further, circuits had to connect up each part of the country to power stations everywhere. Edison set out to manufacture the whole system.

Werner Siemens had constructed the first dynamo in 1866, applying Faraday's theoretical principles in order

playing vinyl discs were introduced in the 1950s, and by 1958 these could also reproduce stereophonic sound.

In more recent years the record has finally been overtaken by two entirely different systems: first magnetic recording on tape, and later the almost indestructible compact disc, operated by laser instead of stylus. Unlike their predecessors these do not depend on Edison's original idea of a stylus vibrating mechanically to produce a practical generator. But it was Thomas Edison who saw the full commercial potential, and he set up the world's first electrical power station at Pearl Street, New York in 1881. It was soon supplying power to thousands of homes and helping to create a rapidly growing market for the electric light.

THE INVENTIONS FACTORY

Perhaps even more significant than this achievement was Edison's approach to the whole process of developing his inventions. In what was at the time a small village, he had set up what was in effect the first industrial research laboratory at Menlo Park, bringing together teams of people to work on projects which he directed. Nothing like it had ever been organised before, and it was a great success.

To develop the electric light bulb he needed people around him who could help with the laborious process of testing different materials for use in the filament. He needed people who could calculate the electrical needs not only of the light bulb but of the entire system of which the light bulb would eventually be a part. Some scientific historians feel that without the organisation of these teams, much of Edison's achievement would not have been possible.

Edison's practical genius ranged over a wide field. His hundreds of other inventions include the carbon microphone which played an essential part in the development of the telephone by allowing high voltages to be used, so making possible long distance communication. He also developed an improved cine-camera and in 1891 he made some of the first commercial moving pictures. He opened a "Kinetoscope Parlour" to exhibit them, but this was one of the rare occasions when he missed an opportunity. He did not forsee that moving pictures would soon be attracting very large audiences and would require powerful projectors. For once he was overtaken by others in this field.

A SETBACK

At the turn of the century he had a serious set back. He threw all his resources into the development of an elaborate method of separating iron ore from rock by a magnetic process. This was suddenly rendered unprofitable when new higher grade ore deposits were found and as a result he lost his entire fortune. With typical

resilience he started up once again, turning his attention to the manufacture and new uses of cement, and the development of an improved storage battery. During the first World War he worked for the United States navy on the development of anti-submarine weapons and periscopes, although by now he was seventy.

Edison was not a great original thinker. His one major scientific discovery was that in certain conditions the vacuum lamp would only permit a one-way flow of electric current. He patented this "Edison Effect" but it was left to J.A. Fleming, an employee at the London branch of the Edison Swan Electric Light Company, to carry out the research which eventually led to the development of the thermionic valve. Most of his discoveries were made by trial and error, but he had a genius for spotting ideas which could be developed – and he was also an energetic persuader of others!

His varied early experience had been a hard school. Edison had learned to be a good judge of people, but he was a hard taskmaster. He did not spare himself and, in his most productive years, would sometimes work for twenty hours a day.

THE FOLK HERO

The newspapers were always interested in what he was doing and helped to make him an American folk hero – his laboratory is now a national monument. This flair for publicity, and his cultivation of the image of the great inventor, were not only something that he enjoyed, he also used them to persuade people to support his business schemes. In the process of promoting himself and his business ventures he also promoted the image of the "age of electricity" as an heroic modern world – not yet darkened by the awesome potential for destruction that technology would later present.

Through his favourite invention he can literally still speak for himself. The following phonograph message was recorded by Edison over eighty years ago, to be played at an electrical exhibition in New York in 1908:

"Those of us who began our labours at the operator's key fifty years ago have been permitted to see and assist in the whole modern industrial development of electricity. In practically every respect civilisation has been revolutionised. We veterans can only urge our successors to realise the measure of their opportunities and their responsibilities in this day of electricity."

CHAPTER XVII

(1867-1912 & 1871-1948)
WILBUR & ORVILLE WRIGHT

Ever since man has gazed in admiration at a seagull in effortless flight, it has been his dream to fly. For centuries the dream remained an elusive one, although such great geniuses as Leonardo Da Vinci had already conceived of flying machines. During the nineteenth century flight of a sort had been achieved: first balloons were all the rage, then from around 1860 real progress in aeronautics was being made. By the end of the century astonished onlookers could watch men in gliders launching off hillsides into the sky to catch the airstreams. Powered, controlled and sustained flight seemed within reach at last, and in 1903 it was the American Wright brothers who achieved the dream.

Wilbur and Orville passed a happy if uneventful childhood in Dayton, Ohio, which remained their home town for the rest of their lives. Their father was a nonconformist Protestant clergyman who quietly supported the flying passions of his sons, although their mother died too early to take part in her children's great successes. Wilbur and Orville were close to each other all their lives although they sometimes disclaimed this; nevertheless Wilbur declared later in life:

"My brother Orville and myself lived together, played together, worked together, and in fact thought together."

Orville was the more excitable of the two, while the reserved and taciturn Wilbur has been regarded as the more natural inventor. All the children were encouraged to experiment and find practical solutions to theoretical problems, and Wilbur had once even built a toy helicopter. By 1892 the two brothers had set up a business to supply the new bicycle craze, and this was to fund them through the early years of their aeronautical investigations.

THE WILD MEN OF FLIGHT

At the end of the nineteenth century, there was a glorious array of eccentric men who risked their necks to achieve flight. The German engineer Otto Lilienthal, and his English counterpart Pilcher were the leaders of their day in the skills of gliding. Both were visionary in believing that the solution to flight lay in imitating the movement of birds' wings. Consequently, they attached huge wing-like structures to their bodies which they could flap by twisting their legs and torso. To achieve lift they threw themselves off hills or were towed into the air. In Pilcher's case this was once done by a pair of

PREPARATION

In 1899 Wilbur wrote to the Smithsonian Institute applying for all available information on aeronautics, explaining humbly:

"I am an enthusiast, but not a crank in the sense that I have some pet theories as to the proper construction of a flying machine. I wish to avail myself of all that is already known and then if possible add my mite to help the

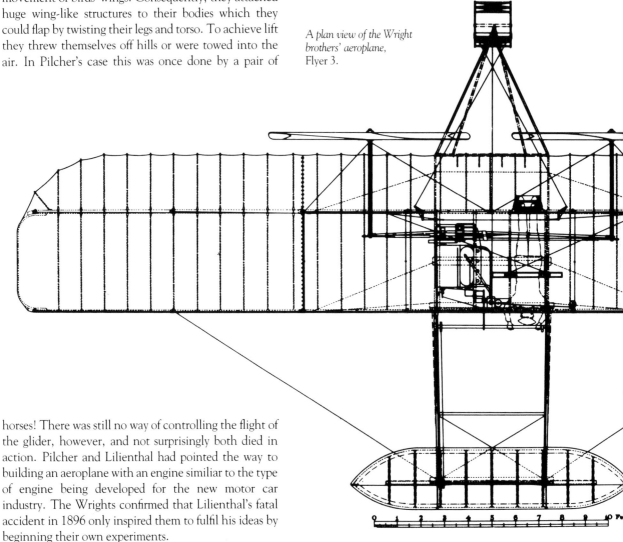

A plan view of the Wright brothers' aeroplane, Flyer 3.

horses! There was still no way of controlling the flight of the glider, however, and not surprisingly both died in action. Pilcher and Lilienthal had pointed the way to building an aeroplane with an engine similiar to the type of engine being developed for the new motor car industry. The Wrights confirmed that Lilienthal's fatal accident in 1896 only inspired them to fulfil his ideas by beginning their own experiments.

future worker who will attain final success."

The brothers read as many books and articles as they could lay their hands on. What struck them was how little general concern there was in mastering how to control a machine – Lilienthal and Pilcher had been entirely at the mercy of their contraptions. Barely a month after steeping themselves in this literature the Wrights began building a flying machine.

EARLY EXPERIMENTS AND PROBLEMS

The first flying machines were constructed and flown as kites with wingspans of five feet. Using such models Wilbur and Orville tested out their theories of control; by far the thorniest problem was that of adjusting and controlling the balance of the flying machine in the air. Nowadays we know through slow motion film that a bird

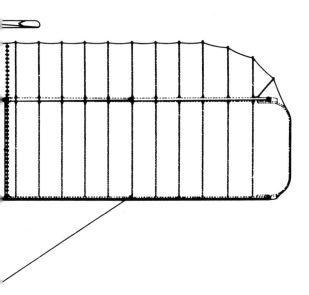

alters the angle of its wings to turn, rise or swoop down, but in 1899 this was an inspired observation which the Wrights had made after watching pigeons in flight. It was to alter the course of flying machine technology.

The next problem was how to twist the wings themselves to imitate the pigeon's action. Wilbur solved this one day when idly twisting the ends of a box in opposite directions: he decided to apply this principle to

the right and left wings on the model, and to his delight, it worked. In the man-carrying Wright flying machines, this twisting of the wings, or wingwarping as it came to be called, would be accomplished by moving a series of warping wires that ran through pulleys to the wingtips.

TESTS AT KITTY HAWK

In the early 1900s experimentation was carried out in the remote bay at Kitty Hawk; the Wrights built a camp, had supplies sent out and spent several weeks, even months there a year. Progress was frustrating. Though their model kites increased in size and advanced technically, they were constantly grappling with the laws of physics. Air pressure, wind velocity and gravity all affected their machine. The response of wingwarping, the difficulties of maintaining fore and aft control, and the continued problem of the lack of lifting power all had to be studied and solved.

Wilbur wrote a paper entitled "Some Aeronautical Experiments" which quickly became indispensible for contemporary would-be aviators.

THE FLYER

Eventually Wilbur and Orville decided they were ready to design a man-carrying glider. Their squat, ugly duckling of a machine was named the *The Flyer*; it had a 40 foot 4 inch wingspan and the outer edges of the aircraft flexed much like modern aircraft. The right wing was longer than the left to provide additional lift for the motor, and its accessories; a droop in the wings themselves ensured that the effects of wind gusts were minimized.

Construction of *The Flyer* was begun in February 1903. But the Wrights soon discovered a snag when it came to finding someone to manufacture its engine. They needed a motor which would have to be especially lightweight, so that a human pilot could be accommodated as well. As the Wrights were at the forefront of aeroplane technology there was no one but themselves who could build this. With the help of a mechanic they finally produced a simplified version of the contemporary automobile motor, in which the engine would turn two propellers with the means of chains, very like a bicycle.

The propellers were the next challenge. They had assumed that they could rely for guidance on the ship-propeller theory – but discovered there was no such

The historic moment on 29th July 1909 when Orville Wright won the U.S. government's first prize for sustained flight.

theory yet! So, after further experimentation, they came up with a propeller theory which tied in beautifully with their principle of adjustable wings. The first Wrights' propellers were just over 8 feet in width. As the engine rotated the propellers, enough speed and wing lift would provide the thrust that propelled the flying machine into the air. The shape and angle of the propeller blades, the speed at which they rotated allowing air to slip backwards through the blades, and the speed of the engine moving forward were all factors mathematically co-ordinated by the Wrights in their quest to build the most efficient propellers of their day. This development was to assure them of success.

HISTORY IS MADE

From October to December 1903 the Wrights experimented with *The Flyer* in a fever of greater secrecy than previous test flights, four miles from Kitty Hawk. They had promised their family to be home by Christmas and so, on a remote beach chosen for its gusty winds amd soft sand in case of crash landings, they decided to go ahead with a test flight on 17 December. Their only witnesses were the men stationed at the life-saving station. Orville lay down in the Flyer, his hips in a padded cradle, wearing his ususal business clothes – suit, starched collar, necktie and cap, and loosened the rope restraining the machine. The following moments made history: the Flyer sped through the air close to 30mph, covering 40 metres in 12 seconds. Of the four flights made that day, the one at noon was of the longest duration: 852 feet were covered in 59 seconds. Orville later described the impact of his first flight in his "Flying" article of 1913.

". . . the first in the history of the world in which a machine carrying a man had raised itself by its own

Orville Wright at
the controls of his
new aeroplane at
Kitty Hawk in the
early 1900's.

power into the air in full flight, had sailed forward without reduction of speed, and had finally landed at a point as high as that from which it started."

When they later calculated their entire costs for this enterprise they came up with a figure of $1,000; this was against Samuel Langley's efforts with his "Aerodrome" who had used $73,000 of government money without success!

COMPETITION AND SECRECY

Over the next few years the Wrights withdrew from the public eye and said nothing to the press; strange stories were beginning to circulate and they worried about espionage. However, as these tales were regarded largely as a joke this did not prove too difficult, despite the fact that men of the stature of Alexander Graham Bell were desperate to advance the study of aeronautics.

Wilbur and Orville still led the field, and by 1904 they were making 14 rounds of Huffman Prairie by air. Though it took some time to convince others of the Flyer's marketability, they eventually won contracts in both France and the States. The Board of Congress quickly recognized its military value and put up $25,000 for further research. After a while the offers to buy up came flooding in.

FURTHER ADVANCES

The Wright Flyers became increasingly sophisticated; by 1908 they were designed to carry two men in a sitting position, and fitted with a more powerful motor. It still took considerable skill to manipulate one of these aircraft, and the Wrights began training pilots. Privately, they had an agreement that only one of them would be in the air at a given time in case anything should happen. In fact, Orville had a few near misses and one particularly serious crash when his passenger died.

Meanwhile, Wilbur was spending much time in France carrying out work. The whole of Europe was held spellbound by his demonstrations, and towns such as Le Mans and Pau became popular pilgrimage spots when Wilbur flew there. In September 1908 Wilbur flew for 1 hour 31 minutes before a crowd of 10,000; the public were ecstatic. One early passenger described how the plane took off:

"I shall never forget the thrill of that first flight. Wilbur Wright and I sat side by side. The machine was catapulted off the ground. It ran along on a rail on a trolley which was left behind when he rose in the air. We climbed up twenty feet and flew twice round the field at tree-top level, at thirty miles an hour. At the turns, the lower wing came within ten feet off the ground. I sat holding onto a strut, and could look straight down between my legs at the ground!"

The taciturn Wilbur remained unmoved by such ecstatic responses and was more concerned with guarding his machine – in those days he even slept in the hangar. Meanwhile in America the Wright Company, founded in 1909, prospered though it took longer for the Wrights to establish themselves commercially in Europe.

END OF AN ERA

Wilbur died unexpectedly in 1912 from typhoid, leaving his brother shattered. Orville lived long enough to become a legend in his own time but maintained a shy distance from press and public. The outbreak of war two years later saw an enormous leap in the fortunes of the Wright Company, but Orville made no significant further innovations in aeronautics. He became involved in a long and bitter feud with the American goverment. Loath to accept that their investment in Langley had bourne so little fruit, the government stubbornly persisted in portraying Langley with all the scientific achievements. Orville eventually emerged triumphant from the battle. He was to witness great advances in aeronautical technology in response to the demands of the Second World War. He died soon after, in 1948.

THEIR IMPACT

What made the Wrights so extraordinary was the combination of their skills as inventors, mechanical engineers, mathematicians and practical mechanics. Wilbur argued that much of their success was a result of "sheer persistance" and "constant practice". But they were certainly not naive about their influence on the twentieth century. Wilbur wrote in a letter to his sister:

"Tell Orville that his flights have revolutionized the world's beliefs regarding the practicality of flight. Even such conservative newspapers as the London Times devote leading editorials to his work and accept human flight as a thing to be regarded as a normal feature of the world's future life."

CHAPTER XVIII

(1863 – 1947)
HENRY FORD

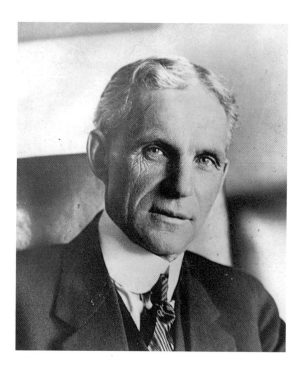

The American car manufacturer Henry Ford probably did more than any one man to influence industrial development in the twentieth century. Not only did he bring motoring to the masses with his now legendary car, the Model T, he also instigated the concept of the production line by which he could double wages and multiply output, thereby changing at a stroke work patterns in America. Henry Ford ushered in an era of mass-consumption which developed in the United States during the twenties and thirties, and spread to Europe when economies revived there after the Second World War. By then, this barely educated man of homespun philosophies had become an American hero in his own time. Ford's extrordinary rise from a poverty-stricken immigrant background to the heights of industrial power was to shine like a beacon of hope to the American worker throughout the Depression years, and long after.

FARM TOIL

The great famine of 1846-9 had driven hundreds and thousands of Irish from their starving country. Among them were Henry Ford's grandparents, who arrived in America in 1847 and settled in the rich farming country near Detroit. Farming was the family occupation for generations: Henry's father inherited the farm which he intended to pass on to his son in turn. It would take him a long time to accept that the farm would not hold his son Henry for long.

Henry was born in 1863, and the toil of farm work was impressed on him at an early age. The hauling and hewing of wood, carrying of water and sowing and harvesting of crops was all done by hand, although the young boy was soon obsessed with the idea that machines should be able to do all this work. Henry used to help out at the local forge, working the bellows and helping to repair the farm implements. One day he

happened to see an agricultural steam engine which had been adapted, by means of a drive belt, to propel the bogie on which it was being transported. These engines were quite common and were used for threshing and sawing wood. That it could also be converted into a road vehicle moving under its own power was a revelation to him.

Henry did not rest until he had put together a model contraption along the same lines, composed of a wooden chassis and a tincan boiler. When it actually managed to cross the farmyard, he was overjoyed. It soon surprised no-one except his father when Henry left for the big city of Detroit to learn more about engineering.

THE DETROIT WATCHMAKER

The pay of a trainee engineer was meagre, and Henry had to eke out his wages by working as a watchmaker in the evenings. During this time he was avidly learning what he could, and also observing for the first time the wasteful layout of the workshops he worked in. Tools and materials were carried back and forth, which delayed the job and frustrated the workers. Already the idea later termed 'time and motion studies' were taking shape in his mind.

Henry Ford was soon promoted, but he left his job to take another, less well-paid, at the Detroit Drydock Company which specialised in boat engines. He was forced to continue his watch repairs, and had an idea that watches could be produced more cheaply if the parts were die-stamped out instead of being laboriously hand made. A jeweller friend was seized with enthusiasm for the idea, but Henry decided there wasn't really enough demand for cheap watches to make it all worthwhile. This was the first of Ford's rare business miscalculations!

FORD'S FIRST MOTOR CAR

Henry returned to the country, bought an eighty-acre farm and got married. It seemed he might settle to the farming life after all, especially after he quickly put his business acumen into practice and set up a profitable sawmill. At the back of his mind, however, was the old

Henry Ford admiring the very first Ford car, next to the ten millionth model.

Working on the Ford engine in an early Ford Motor Company production line, in around 1914.

pull of the steam engine which could move under its own power. Ford began to experiment again, but soon appreciated that the enormous weight of the boilers, combined with the water it had to carry and the necessary solidity of the undercarriage, would cause it to use most of the generated power just to move on the rough rural American roads. A German inventor had already made an engine that could run on coal gas. However, this required bulky bags to store the gas and was also very dangerous, as the gas was liable to explode. Its main recommendation was the engine's lightness, and Ford knew he could make a better one – to run on gasoline.

Ford was essentially an instinctive engineer. He had never been formally educated in mathematics and science, nor was he trained in the recent European technological advances in motor car engineering by Rolls and Royce, Bouton, Panhard, Daimler and Benz. However, he had an uncanny instinct for efficient engine design, and would often walk into the room and be able to put his finger on the one correct solution among the several which engineers had been debating for days. This instinct was to make his fortune.

THE FORD MOTOR COMPANY

In 1903 Ford established the Ford Motor Company after scratching together for investors. His aim was to produce a $500 motor car, at a time when the average price of cars produced by the American Association of Licensed Automobile Manufacturers (ALAM) was nearer $1400.

According to Ford, the key factor in automobile design was the question of weight. A light, powerful engine was required, but to make the most of the power, the bodywork had to be as light as possible. Since the car was then a luxury item, seating was naturally well padded and expensively panelled, adding unnecessary weight to the chassis – in fact in everything but motive power, the early vehicles were just like horse-drawn carriages.

Ford's innovation was to be an absolutely rudimentary design. The engine would be fuelled by petroleum, and not only would it be built with standardized parts, but a string of depots would also be established across the country for the easy replacement of spare parts. His dream was manufacturing cars for the masses, and by appealing to the mass market, he calculated that the increased sales would more than offset the vastly reduced price.

By 1908, after several years of experimenting with vehicle designs, Ford began to produce the famous 'Model T' – "Available in any colour", he famously declared, "so long as it's black."

THE PRODUCTION LINE

The new cheap Ford was ugly, temperamental and uncomfortable. But Ford's radical gamble became a sensational success. People joked about it but they loved it all the same, giving it the nickname "Tin Lizzie". Over the next twenty years Americans were to buy fifteen million Model T's.

What Ford had up his sleeve next was even more extraordinary. His early experimenting with time-saving processes, combined with a series of contemporary breakthroughs in machining and manufacturing engine parts, lead to his perfection of the idea of the production line. Instead of wandering from job to job, a conveyor belt would now bring all the parts of the job to the worker.

What had previously been a laborious task for a skilled worker was broken down into a thousand tiny, routine tasks. Workers did not even need to speak the language, and thousands of immigrants fed into the car factories as a result. A series of carefully timed assembly lines fed into one main line, to produce the final product. As Ford had predicted, this saved so much time that output leapt up, enabling him to introduce the Five Dollar Week, an eight hour day, and the possibility for workers to share in the profits of the company.

This was the biggest sensation of all, being double the average car worker's wages at the time. Skilled engineers queued outside his factory gates, and industrialists up and down the country condemned Ford's action, convinced it would lead to labour unrest as they could not match such conditions. The political Left were unhappy too, once they had got over the shock of this Utopian novelty: having given his workers everything he considered necessary for maximum production and worker

Henry Ford with his son, Edsel.

satisfaction, he had no patience at all with the idea of trade unions to represent the views of his workforce. To the outrage of the American trade union movement, all unions were banned in his factories. Ford was undeterred by the uproar at both extremes of the political spectrum and went on to establish a Sociological department to counsel workers, gave them housing support where necessary and generally introduced a more humane attitude to working conditions and morale, which was an unheard of notion at the time.

LEGAL BATTLES

Meanwhile the ALAM were alarmed at the way the young manufacturer was undercutting their firms, and sued Ford over patent rights. What was at issue was an attempt to control all independent enterprise, and Ford fought the action for seven years, at a cost of over a million dollars. Victory was his in the end, and very shortly the ALAM ceased to exist.

Released from the monopoly control of the ALAM, smaller companies sprang up like mushrooms everywhere, and soon Ford's production system was in competition with other manufacturers. A speeding up of his own system became imperative to maintain profits, and gradually the benevolent dictatorship of his factory system became an increasingly authoritarian trap. The workforce was harshly regulated, with break times kept to a minimum and rigidly enforced. Ford began to use secret service men and factory spies, but when he was accused of shackling his workers to eight hours of such repetitive tedium that a chimpanzee could be trained to do the same work, his only response was a genuine frown of incomprehension.

Ford, who had set out with such idealism to change working conditions, had become increasingly inflexible and autocratic. Even his ideas on pacifism were soon to change.

THE PEACE SHIP

At the outbreak of the 1914-18 war in Europe, Ford was so vociferously opposed to the conflict that he charted a 'Peace Ship' to take a large, disparate and, unfortunately, squabbling group of pacifists to Europe to argue for an end to hostilities. The whole enterprise ended as a fiasco, and when America finally entered the conflict, Ford threw himself wholeheartedly into the war effort.

Although he became famous for the throwaway quip, 'history is bunk', he experienced for himself the warning that those who ignore history are doomed to repeat it. With the outbreak of World War Two, Ford again overcame his great reluctance to support a war and directed his huge manufacturing capacity to the production of planes and tanks.

By now, the grand old man American industry had begun to show his clay feet: he published a distasteful series of anti-Semetic articles and when he sued a newspaper that had accused him of anarchy and ignorance, he unwittingly revealed in court just how child-like his reasoning was. Curiously enough, although the newspapers had a field day at Ford's expense, Ford's embarrassing courtroom performance only served to endear him more to the American public.

Meanwhile the Model T was becoming obsolete in the twenties, and Ford was only convinced of the fact with the greatest of difficulty. His autocratic grip on the Ford empire almost proved to be its ruin. The delay in introducing the new 'Model A' cost him his previous dominance of the market, but he soon recovered this and opened factories in England to cater for the continent.

THE FORD FOUNDATION

Although Ford remained stubborn and frustratingly obstinate to the end, his unceasing work continued well into his eightieth year. "Go to work. That's the answer to everything" was his invariable advice, although many people also regarded him as a man of wit and humour and his jokes were widely repeated. Ford had become a legend, and towards the end of his life he rediscovered his philanthropic instincts and spent enormous sums on establishing the Ford Foundation in 1936, which would fund artistic, scientific, educational and charitable causes.

In 1947 this towering character died peacefully in his sleep. He left behind an industrial system that spread around the world – even to the young Communist Russia, where Lenin had recognised the Ford system as the best way the country could bring itself up to date. Only now, seventy years after Ford developed his mass-production system, can it be said that we are entering a Post-Fordian era. In transport and in industrial technique, Ford had dominated the century.

CHAPTER XIX

(1845 – 1923)
WILHELM KONRAD RÖNTGEN

The last decade of the nineteenth century was a time of great excitement in science and some of this excitement spilled out of the laboratories to be shared by the general public. One of the most significant events of this period was the discovery of a new form of radiation by the German physicist Wilhelm Röntgen. X-rays caught the public imagination in a way that few other scientific discoveries have done, and there were several claims by charlatans that other mysterious rays with miraculous properties had been discovered. The idea that the new rays could see right through the body to the skeleton was sensational, and was the source of many jokes as well as great hopes that X-rays would lead to important advances in medicine.

A WATERSHED

In the last quarter of the nineteenth century most scientists believed that they had an fairly complete understanding of nature. They realised that there were still many interesting gaps in their knowledge to be filled but the overall picture seemed to be increasingly clear. In hindsight there were already some small rips in the fabric, for example Maxwell's theories (Chapter VI), but the great theoretician Helmholtz had said, "the final aim of science is to resolve itself into mechanics", and Newton's approach still seemed to be extending triumphantly to all branches of science.

The tide turned quite unexpectedly as the century came towards its end. The discovery of X-rays in 1895, the equally unexpected discovery of radioactivity in the following year and of the electron in 1897, were part of a sudden change that marks one of the great watersheds in human thought and history. By the first decade of the new century scientists had to begin to grapple with entirely new ways of thinking about the world. The certainties of Newton's picture no longer fitted many of the new facts, and after the work of men like Einstein (Chapter XXIV) and Rutherford (Chapter XXV),

An early instance of treatment by Röntgen rays at St. Bartholemew's hospital in 1912.

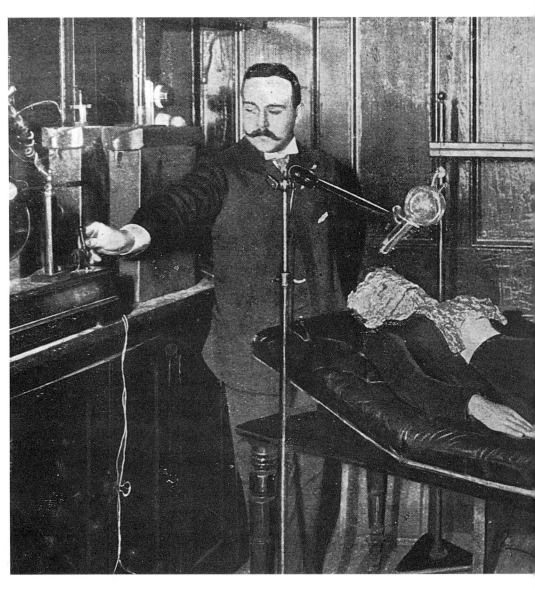

Newton's "majestic clockwork" had to give place to something altogether less familiar. As Sir James Jeans, the Astronomer Royal, wrote in 1930: "the universe begins to look more like a great thought than like a great machine."

The discovery of X-rays and radioactivity were not only an important part of this revolution in scientific thought, but also soon had many important practical consequences. Even if the new ideas seemed remote, the use of both X-rays and radium in medicine came quite

quickly and many of the applications of the new science began to have an increasing effect on the lives of ordinary people. By the middle of the century the harnessing of nuclear energy had changed the course of history and even posed the question of whether there was to be any future (Chapter XXVI).

CATHODE RAYS

Wilhelm Röntgen studied in Holland and Switzerland. He went on to a number of teaching posts before being

pumps made it possible to produce very low pressures. As in many other cases, improvements in apparatus or technique opened the way for new discoveries to be made.

It was known that when a tube was pumped out to a high vacuum, the remaining trace of gas glowed if a high voltage was passed through it. (This effect was later to be used in "neon tubes" for advertising signs). Then in 1878 Sir William Crookes (1832 – 1919) discovered that some form of radiation streamed off from the negative terminal, or cathode. These rays travelled through the tube in a straight line and where they hit its walls the glass glowed. In 1895 Röntgen, like many other physicists, was studying these cathode rays. They were known to be deflected by a magnet, and to have a very short range in air, but their nature was still a puzzle.

A NEW KIND OF RAY

At the time of his discovery, Röntgen was investigating what happened when cathode rays struck a metal target which he placed inside the tube. In order to detect any rays which passed out of the tube he was using a paper screen coated with a barium salt which glowed if it was struck by the rays. The Crookes tube itself was wrapped in black paper.

On 8th November 1895 he was setting up a new experiment. When all was ready he darkened the room and switched on the current. To his great surprise he noticed that the paper screen was glowing brightly, although at the time it was about two metres away from the apparatus. Cathode rays could not travel more than a few centimetres through the air, so he knew that some quite different kind of radiation was being produced. Röntgen at once realised that he had come upon something both entirely new and very important.

He was now in his element and he worked intensively over the next few weeks to find out as much as he could about these new rays. He was always a serious man – he even planned the holidays that he spent hiking with his wife in the Alps with scientific precision. But now he became totally immersed in his discovery. He turned up irregularly for meals and often dashed back to the laboratory leaving his food scarcely touched. He hardly talked to his wife, Bertha, who recalled that for her these were "simply terrible days".

What struck him most of all was the extremely

appointed professor of physics and director of the new Physical Institute at Würtzburg, Germany, in 1888. His research had included work on heat and elasticity, but in 1895, like several others, he was experimenting on the passage of electricity through gases at low pressures. This line of investigation had been started by Michael Faraday (Chapter V), although at the time it did not appear to be of major significance, compared with his other achievements. It was to bear important fruit during the next thirty years when increasingly efficient vacuum penetrating nature of the rays. He described, for example, how a bound book of a thousand pages cast almost no shadow on the fluorescent screen. Most other materials were equally transparent to the rays, although he made the important observation that when he held his hand in front of the screen: "the darker shadow of the bones is seen within the faint shadow of the hand itself". Only dense metals such as platinum and lead seemed to present any real obstruction. Unlike cathode rays these new rays were unaffected by magnets, but although he tried using lenses of various materials, he was unable to get any direct evidence that they could be refracted like light. Nevertheless he came to the tentative conclusion that they were some form of "vibrations in the ether", related to light and ultra violet radiation. Soon he had obtained enough information to publish a paper on "A new kind of Ray".

THE IMPACT OF X-RAYS

It was natural that other scientists should be excited by this discovery of something so unexpected, but he was no doubt quite bemused by the reaction of the general public. The greatest popular impact was made by the X-ray pictures which accompanied his paper. These included a photograph of his wife's hand, clearly showing her bones and the ring she was wearing. The medical possibilities were obvious at once and before long X-rays had become established as an important new method of diagnosis. But after a while there began to be reports of unfortunate injuries suffered by some of the scientists who had rushed so eagerly to investigate the new rays. It became apparent that prolonged exposure to the radiation can do serious damage to the body; but this was the beginning of another important application of X-rays. With carefully controlled and targeted doses, as used today in radiotherapy, tumours could be treated for the first time, even when situated in parts of the body which made an operation impossible.

Röntgen had not been able to prove for certain whether his rays were a form of radiation, as he believed, or a stream of particles of some type, so he gave them the neutral title of x-rays until the matter could be resolved. Although they were re-named Röntgen rays in his honour, their original name, with its hint of mystery, has stuck.

There was a similar problem about the nature of the

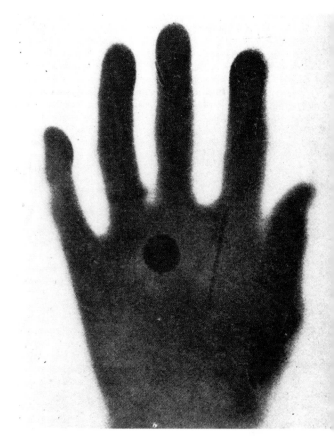

less spectacular cathode rays but in 1897 Sir J.J. Thompson (1856 – 1940) discovered that these were in fact a stream of negatively charged particles and they became known as electrons. That solved one problem but it created an even greater puzzle, because electrons appeared to be far smaller than atoms which, almost by definition, were supposed to be the smallest possible particles of matter. This was one of the challenges taken up by Ernest Rutherford (Chapter XXV).

Confirmation of the nature of X-rays took some time. Max von Laue (1879 – 1960) was convinced, like Röntgen, that they were similar to light, but of a very much shorter wavelength which made the necessary experiments on diffraction difficult to carry out. The usual diffraction gratings of microscopically small lines engraved on glass were be far too large to show any effects, so von Laue suggested that it might be possible to use the regular layers of atoms within a crystal as a grating instead. It was not until 1912 that he was finally able to

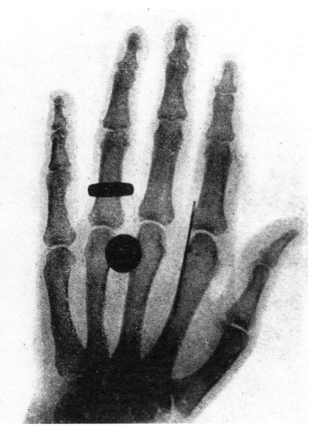

Röntgen's first X-rays of his wife's hand. The left hand photograph was taken by Becquerel rays after an exposure of one hour, the right by Röntgen rays.

prove that X-rays are part of the electromagnetic spectrum, and that they had a wavelength about a thousand times smaller than visible light.

THE DISCOVERY OF RADIOACTIVITY

A year after Röntgen's discovery, X-rays played an important part in another major scientific development, although more by muddle and luck than by design. Henri Becquerel (1852 – 1908) was interested in the fluorescence of uranium salts. Like several other materials, these glow for a short time after they have been exposed to a bright light. When he heard about Röntgen's experiments, especially the glowing of the paper screen, Becquerel wondered whether fluorescence and X-rays were somehow always linked together and he

planned an experiment to test this. The idea was to expose some crystals of a uranium salt to bright sunlight while they were on top of a photographic plate which was wrapped in thick black paper. If the fluorescence was accompanied by the formation of X-rays, these would penetrate the paper and expose the plate, giving a silhouette of the crystals.

He prepared an experiment on the 26th of February 1896, but could not go ahead because the weather turned cloudy. So, after they had had hardly any exposure to sunlight, he put the plates back in the drawer, with the crystals still in place. He described what happened next:

"Since the sun did not show itself again for several days I developed the plates on the 1st of March, expecting to find very feeble images. The silhouettes appeared, on the contrary, with great intensity."

The great puzzle was where this energy was coming from. The fluorescence that he was originally investigating is simply the trapping of some energy from the sunlight, and this is all given out again in less than a second. But he found that some samples which he had kept completely in the dark were still giving out radiation just as strongly two months later. He did some further experiments with uranium metal itself. This does not give any fluorescent effect, but the mysterious radiation was even stronger still. Becquerel had discovered radioactivity, but he was unable to explain what was going on.

The investigation was taken up by Pierre (1859 – 1906) and Marie Curie (1867 – 1934), and they shared the Nobel Prize for Physics with Henri Becquerel in 1903 for their pioneering work in this entirely new field. (Marie Curie was to win an unprecedented second Nobel Prize eight years later, this time in Chemistry, for her further work on radioactivity and the discovery of Radium). It remained for Ernest Rutherford (Chapter XXV) to show the full importance of Becquerel's discovery and to find the explanation for radioactivity.

X-RAY CRYSTALLOGRAPHY

The wavelength of ordinary light is very small, on a human scale, but atoms are smaller still. It is therefore impossible to "see" atoms, or to get precise information about anything on the atomic scale, by using light. When Lawrence Bragg, then a young research student at

Cambridge, heard about von Laue's experiment, he realised that X-rays might be a suitable tool for probing the structure of crystals, because their wavelength (about one ten thousandth of a millionth of a metre) is similar to the distance between atoms. Working with his father, William Henry Bragg who was at that time professor of physics at Leeds, he carried out many of the experiments which led to the new science of X-ray crystallography. This technique made it possible for the first time to map the internal structure of substances. It gave many new theoretical insights and it also has important practical applications in the testing of materials. Sir Lawrence Bragg went on to become Director of the Royal Institution where he continued to make many important contributions to this field.

Yet another new science, molecular biology, was opened up when information became available about the architecture of the complex molecules present in plants and animals. Today, when a new drug is being developed, the structure of its molecules and the way in which it works within the body are probed by using X-ray crystallography. More important still, it has led to great advances in our understanding of the processes of life itself. For example, the crucial evidence needed by Crick and Watson in their work on the structure of DNA was obtained in this way. This was the first major step in understanding how genetic information is passed on and it marked the start of one of the most significant and rapidly growing areas of present day science.

BLACK HOLES
At the opposite extreme of the scale of nature, X-rays are also providing new information for astronomers. The atmosphere absorbs any X-rays that reach the earth from space, but with the coming of artificial satellites it has been possible to put X-ray detectors in orbit above the atmosphere. A new window on nature has been opened as a result, one which gives information especially about the very violent events that take place in some distant parts of the galaxy. For example the immense heating that is caused as material is sucked into a black hole would betray itself in bursts of X-rays. Several examples of black holes have now been identified by means of X-ray astronomy, confirming one of the most unimaginable predictions of the theory of relativity.

When chance plays an important part in a discovery, as it did in the case of X-rays and radioactivity, there is a tendency to over-emphasise the luck involved. Even before he made his great discovery, Wilhelm Röntgen was recognised to be one of the most outstanding experimentalists of his day and he was ideally qualified to follow up his chance observation. In 1901 he was awarded the first of the Nobel Prizes for Physics to mark the importance of his work. Almost a century later the ripples from his discovery are still spreading out: from the routine X-ray photographs taken by our dentist to the host of new techniques of present-day science.

Professor Röntgen himself, though, might not have approved of this description of his work. He severely criticised attempts to explain science to the non-specialist because, he said, this is just "furthering a superficial knowledge, which is worse and more dangerous than none at all." Let us hope that, for once, he was mistaken.

STRAND-JDYLL Á LA RÖNTGEN

This German postcard at the end of the 19th century depicts the saucy delights of X-rays at the seaside.

CHAPTER XX

(1874 – 1937)
GUGLIELMO MARCONI

In every field of human endeavour, a spurt of progress is usually made by a gifted individual who has put together the pieces of a jigsaw to produce something completely new. Such a man was Guglielmo Marconi, often described as "the father of radio". Many times in his career, he was accused of merely being a 'cribber' of other people's ideas, but he modestly replied:

I doubt very much whether there has ever been a case of a useful invention in which all the theory, all the practical applications and all the apparatus were the work of one man."

Although there are several international figures, notably the Russian scientist Popov, who could claim to have invented radio, it was Marconi who put the radio waves to work.

THE COSMOPOLITAN AMATEUR

Just as Marconi's inventions were regarded as an amalgam of ideas, Marconi's appearance owed much to various influences. On his first visit to America, A reporter wrote:

"When you meet Signor Marconi, you're bound to notice that he's a "for'ner." His suit of clothes is English. In stature he is French. His boot heels are Spanish military. His hair and moustache are German. His mother is Irish. His father is Italian. And altogether, there's little doubt that Marconi is a thorough cosmopolitan."

Marconi was probably the last of the gifted amateurs, who was able to use the more academic ideas of others and apply them to what was becoming an urgent

An early electric ship telegraph system on HMS Theseus, in 1904.

communications problem, as rail and steam power were drawing the continents closer together.

THE NEED TO COMMUNICATE

Throughout the nineteenth century, attempts were made to find a solution to the problem of long-distance communication. Needles were made to quiver and oscillate, sometimes to indicate the letters of the alphabet on a board, and sometimes to make bells and gongs sound in different tones. The morse code was widely used in these efforts, and indeed, a workable telegraph system was in existence – even submarine cables had been laid across oceans to carry the staccato dots and dashes. It was Marconi who conceived the startling notion that messages, in morse at first, but later even via the human voice, could be carried through the 'ether' independent of wires, on radio 'waves'. Small wonder then, that his invention came to be known as the 'wireless.'

THE SELF-TAUGHT INVENTOR

Marconi was born on 25th April, 1874 in the northern Italian town of Bologna. His father was a prosperous Italian banker, and his mother an heiress of the Irish whiskey distilling family – the Jameson's. Although Gulielmo was born and brought up in Italy, his mother always spoke English to him, and this was to become an enormous advantage to Marconi in later years.

Even from his childhood he was interested in magnets and electric currents made from home-made batteries. His relationship with his mother was very close, and she

A 1922 model of the Marconiphone broadcaster-receiver, used with headphones, it was the earliest of the commercially produced wireless sets.

A beam radio station in Grimsby, for transmissions of the Empiradio network to India and Australia. It was set up by the Marconi Company in 1920.

took a lively interest in his experiments and tutored him well into his teens. Although he never went to university his mother arranged for him to attend lectures by such notable scientific figures as Professor Vincenzo Rosa at Livorno, and Professor Augusto Righi at the University of Bologna. Marconi also read very widely and frequently reproduced experiments he found described in books which he borrowed from the Bologna University library.

As he grew older, the cost of materials for his experiments became a serious problem, and on one occasion he even sold his new pair of boots in order to buy equipment. For a long time his father thought of this hobby as a profound waste of time, and discouraged him. He even destroyed experiments which his son had set up and tried to smash the plates pegged to a long wire – only to be flung off by electrical curents when Guglielmo threw the switch. Eventually, however, the clash of wills subsided, and he advanced his son sufficient funds to enable him to continue experimenting. Soon, he was sending signals clear across his father's estate, using Morse code.

*The 'Marconiphone',
patented by the young
Marconi in 1896.*

PROGRESS TO ENGLAND

An important discovery he made was the simultaneous use of two earths, one for sending and one for receiving signals. This greatly increased the range for transmission. In addition, he discovered that the higher he raised the aerials above the ground, the greater the increase in the range of communication. By the end of 1895, he was able to send messages over distances of two miles.

By this time, Signor Marconi was convinced of the worth of his son's activities, and after taking advice from the local doctor and priest – a normal prudent procedure in Italian country districts – it was decided to bring Guglielmo's discoveries to the attention of the Italian government. To everyone's great disappointment, no-one in the government seemed very interested at all.

Guglielmo refused to leave the matter there and decided to set off for England. He had an idea that his new system might be useful for ship to shore communication. England had a great navy – it was logical to try his luck there. Accompanied by his mother and dressed in a Sherlock Holmes hat and long overcoat, he crossed the Channel, only to have his precious equipment damaged by prying customs officials, who feared it might be an anarchist's bomb.

MARCONI THE BUSINESS MAN

Signore Marconi had passed onto his son all of his business acumen. One of the first things Marconi did was to take out a patent for his system of telegraphy, and then give a demonstration in front of officials from the General Post Office, the British Army and Navy, on Salisbury Plain. He rigged up aerials over twenty eight metres high and successfully achieved transmissions over a distance of almost two miles.

Marconi gained enormous fame overnight, and he quickly had to prove that he was his father's son, otherwise he and his invention would have been soon parted. It was clear to all that enormous fortunes could be made here, and he was besieged with offers to sell his patent. The Italian bank even offered 300,000 lira. Marconi ignored all approaches, firstly because he felt that further improvements were needed but also because he was sure that his invention was worth very much more than what he was being offered. In later life he recalled:

"The English believed at the start that they had to do

with a young man of scant experience who could be easily dominated."

They soon found out that he was as hard-headed in his business dealings as he was in his scientific work. He founded his own company, Marconi's Telegraph Co. Ltd.

RADIO OVER THE SEA

After further experiments on Salisbury Plain Marconi increased his range to four and a half miles, using kites to take his aerials to a great height. As he did so he noticed that the slope of his aerial had an important effect on the direction of the transmission. However he still did not know how his apparatus would function over water. Experts were of the opinion that radio waves would not follow the contours of the earth, and instead of curving parallel to the globe, would simply shoot off into space at a tangent.

Again Marconi was undeterred. The masts of ships were ideally suited to aerials, and it was not long before the navies of France, Germany, Britain and Italy, together with several major shipping companies, had adopted his system. It soon proved its worth in summoning aid to ships in distress, fog or bad weather, enabling lifeboats to be launched in good time and so save lives that might otherwise have been lost.

The next great test would be to send a message across the Atlantic, and see once and for all if the sceptics were right. It was the biggest gamble of his life, costing over fifty thousand pounds. He erected a transmitter a hundred times more powerful than anything he had used before at Poldhu in Cornwall, and succeeded in sending signals to St. Catherine's Point on the Isle of Wight, over 186 miles away. Signals were then received even further than that at Crookhaven on the west coast of Ireland. Marconi was overjoyed, although a fierce storm wrecked his Cornwall transmitter. He was now ready to try the Atlantic experiment.

THE CROSSING OF THE ATLANTIC

Marconi set up his equipment at the port of St. John's in Newfoundland, off the Canadian coast. He had arranged for the morse letter 'S' to be broadcast from Poldhu every ten minutes, which he hoped would be picked up on his 122 metres high aerial. He described the tense moments leading up to the trial which would spell

The home wireless set soon became the focus
of family entertainment before the Second World War.

A confident young Marconi shortly after his arrival in England,
photographed with his apparatus for "telegraphy without wires."

success or disaster for his venture:

"It was shortly after midday on 12th December 1901 that I placed a single earphone to my ear and started listening. The receiver on the table was very crude – a few coils and condensers and a coherer, no valves, no amplifier, not even a crystal . . . Suddenly there sounded a sharp click of the "tapper" as it struck the coherer, showing me that something was coming, and I listened intently. Unmistakeably, the three sharp clicks corresponding to three dots sounded in my ear . . . the electric waves which were being sent out from Poldhu had travelled the Atlantic, serenely ignoring the curvature of the earth which so many doubters considered to be a fatal obstacle . . . I knew that the day on which I would be able to send full messages across the Atlantic was not so far distant."

THE NOBEL PRIZE

It still was not clear why the radio waves should have

followed the curvature of the earth. Two scientists at the time suggested that a layer of ions – electrified particles – high above the earth might be reflecting the waves back down to earth again. This was only proved to be correct twenty years later.

In the meantime, Marconi shared the Nobel Prize for Physics, to everyone's surprise, including his own, as he had always regarded himself as an inventor and entrepreneur rather than a serious physicist.

Marconi's next challenge was to combat atmospheric interference, which was to bedevil radio communications from then on. Marconi also met with enormous opposition from the vested interests of cable-linked telegraphy. Huge sums had been invested in these cables, and now wireless threatened to compete successfully against them since the costs were so much less.

SOS

Meanwhile, wireless appeals for help from stricken vessels at sea began to save lives on a grand scale. In 1909 the liner *Republic* suffered great damage when she was accidentally rammed in darkness and fog by the Italian ship *Florida*. Due to the heroic efforts of a young Marconi radio operator, help was summoned that saved more than 1,700 lives. Three years later, on 14th April 1912, the 'unsinkable' ship the *Titanic* struck an iceberg. The wireless operator kept sending out the newly adopted international 'SOS' signal – Save Our Souls – until the ship went down, and he himself died. Although 1,503 lives were lost that night, 703 were picked up by the liner *Carpathia* which had been summoned to her aid. These terrible accidents soon made ship captains realise the importance of having a radio operator on duty at all times.

The Marconi Company set up wireless telegraph stations in Russia, Finland, Canada and Hawaii, but competitors soon caught up, most notably the German *Telefunken* Company. But so far, the only messages being transmitted were in crackling morse code.

TRANSMISSION OF THE HUMAN VOICE

Further developments in valve technology in America made it possible by 1915 to transmit actual speech, through a series of continuous waves. An historic broadcast was made from the town of Arlington near Washington to Paris – over 3,500 miles away.

In Europe the Great War of 1914-18 had just broken out, and the possibilities for radio were seen as so tremendous that the technology was developed quickly to meet military needs. One of the few benefits to arise from that horrific war was the developments of shortwave transmissions, which were found to be much more suitable for the human voice. If the signals were concentrated into a narrow beam, they could be picked up strongly at very long distances, especially at night, and the shortwave aerials also did not need to be so enormously high. By the time peace came, millions of sailors and soldiers had been introduced to the wireless.

RADIO AROUND THE WORLD

The new short wave was adopted by the British Empire to communicate with its territories around the world, and long after the Empire's disintegration the system continued to be adopted in many countries. In 1914 Marconi had ventured to predict:

"Perhaps some day everyone will have a receiver in their house, and, from a central station, news of all kinds will be constantly sent out . . ."

His prediction was to come true very quickly. By 1920 the first regular broadcast service in Britain began, and two years later the British Broadcasting Corporation was formed, a public company with a royal charter. Similarly, in America commercial advertising companies were not slow to see the possibilities of reaching into millions of homes – though at first only with the aid of tiny, crackling crystal sets.

Marconi acquired a splendid yacht fitted out like a floating laboratory. he sailed around the globe to monitor test signals while his company built transmitters around the world. He was showered with honours, especially in his native Italy, where he was made a marquis and a senator. Marconi became a natural and favourite ambassador for his country, and he even signed the peace treaties for Italy with Bulgaria and Germany in 1919.

When he died in 1937, the news was broadcast to the world over the medium he had spent his life perfecting. Many countries ceased broadcasting for two minutes, beginning at 6.0pm, whilst operators stood with their heads bowed by their apparatus: a solemnly appropriate gesture to the man who had made the ether speak.

CHAPTER XXI

(1888 – 1946)
JOHN LOGIE BAIRD

In 1926 the *Times* newspaper reported cautiously on the first public demonstration of television:
"The image transmitted was faint and often blurred, but substantiated a claim that through the 'televisor', as Mr Baird has named his apparatus, it is possible to transmit and reproduce instantly the details of movement and such things as the play of expression on the face."

Cautious acknowledgement dogged John Logie Baird all his life. Despite being one of this century's greatest inventors, his achievements have suffered a puzzling degree of disparagement and neglect. Baird is primarily remembered for producing the world's first true television pictures, and his enduring influence in the whole field of telecommunications is often overlooked. He became a world leader in pioneering colour, three-dimensional and facsimile television, was ahead of his time in producing the first video recordings, and made vital contributions to the fields of fibre optics and radar.

A SCOTTISH EDUCATION

Baird's enterprising nature was apparent from his earliest childhood. He was born in 1888 in the prosperous Scottish town of Helensburgh, the youngest of four children. His childhood was not a particulary happy one: from the age of six Baird was sent to a series of educational establishments which the bright boy found unremittingly loathsome and tedious. Baird received no scientific training of any sort, but this lack only served to channel his enthusiasm for science all the more. All that remained to him of those days, he would later say, was the continual ill-health which he blamed on the endless cold showers he suffered at school.

Baird mentally escaped this grim environment by continuously inventing new gadgets. He was fascinated with photography and modified his camera to take pictures of himself whilst asleep. By the age of twelve, Baird had built a private telephone exchange connecting him with four friends. A year later he had even designed

An early colour transmission in 1943.

and installed an electricity supply at his home.

The developing technology of aviation was another fascination, and the young boy constructed a precarious glider with two kites, hauled it onto the roof, and having failed to cajole a friend into taking the controls, climbed in. It snapped in two and nose-dived spectacularly into the ground . . . Baird would never fly again.

THE BLACK MAGIC MAN
In 1906 Baird began studies in electrical engineering at the Royal Technical College in Glasgow. Here he spent eight years – with interruptions of ill-health – immersing himself into the new technology. During the next decade his eclectic inventiveness found new outlets: he attempted to produce a cure for piles (and found he couldn't sit for several days); set up the Baird Undersock Company and made a killing from selling watertight socks; tried to create a diamond; and even manufactured jam in the Caribbean, earning himself the nickname "Obeah", the Black Magic Man.

Meanwhile the quest for television had been under-way at least half a century before Baird's breakthrough, but Baird had been pondering the problem from the age of thirteen:

"Even at that time I had begun to think about the possibility of sending pictures by telephone . . . But whenever I mentioned it, the very idea struck people as fantastic . . . If sound waves could be converted into waves of another sort and sent over wires, why not light waves?"

THE BREAKTHROUGH
Baird continued to fund his investigations by his own enterprises, and through investments from friends. He was soon immersed in the technical problems of producing a television picture. To achieve this it was necessary to convert light from the scene of intended televisation into an electrical signal for transmission, and then convert this via the receiver into an image on a screen. The selenium cell was known to convert light into electricity, but reception of a detailed picture required line by line scanning, and selenium could not produce enough electricity for this. The first scanning device was the Nipkow disc invented by Paul Nipkow in 1884: this had a spiral series of square holes to let light through in strips as it rotated. Virtually no progress had been made since Nipkow, and Baird was occupied for many years with the problem of how to amplify selenium cell currents. His breakthrough came when he realized this could be simply achieved with a radio valve.

*John Baird during a
television rehearsal
in 1943.*

*Baird tuning in to an early
commercial television set
of the 1940's.*

SUCCESS

Baird recorded his first success as October 1925. At the time he was living and working in rented rooms on very little money, using makeshift and dangerous equipment constructed from his forays into scrapyards and antique shops. Minor explosions were not infrequent!

He had constructed himself a Nipkow disc from cardboard, mounted it on a darning needle, borrowed a motor from an electric fan to rotate it and added a vast array of torch batteries and lamps. One day he began receiving varying degrees of light and shade in the pictures of the ventriloquist's dummy he used as a model. Baird later wrote:

"I ran down the flight of stairs to Mr. Cross's office and seized by the arm his office boy, William Taynton, hauled him upstairs and put him in front of the transmitter . . . I pushed his head into position. This time he came through and on the screen I saw the flickering but clearly recognisable image of William's face – the first face to be seen on television – and he had to be bribed 2s 6d. for the privilege of this distinction."

TELEVISION GOES PUBLIC

From 1924-26 Baird worked hard to improve the sensitivity of photoelectric cells. He found that the use of lensed discs concentrated light even more effectively. But it was in April 1925 that Baird hit the headlines like never before. For a fee of £20 pounds per week Baird agreed to demonstrate television in the London department store of Selfridges, for three weeks. The queues were never-ending, despite the cool response to the breakthrough by the store's directors:

"The picture is flickering and defective and at present only simple pictures can be sent successfully."

It was enough for the public. Baird became a centre of media attention and was to remain so during the inter-war years.

The original model of Baird's first television apparatus, with the puppet which served as the first televised image in October 1925.

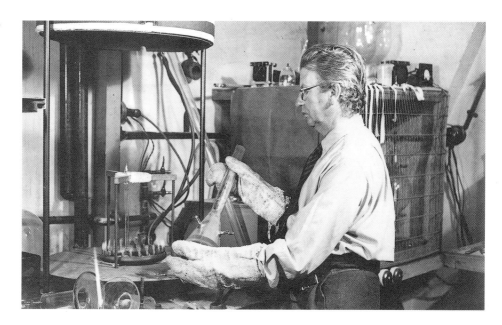

Baird adjusting an early television tube in 1943.

LONG DISTANCE TV

After 26 January 1926, when television was officially launched before members of the Royal Institute, it seemed that Baird's future was secured. Later in the same year the Post Office issued him with the first TV licence. By this time Baird was eager to prove that television could be transmitted over long distance: this he achieved on May 24th 1927 in a transmission from London to Glasgow.

There was no stopping television from now on. The first transatlantic transmission, between London and New York took place on 8th February 1928. Baird International shares leapt; the Prime Minister Ramsay MacDonald sent personal thanks for the installation of a television at 10 Downing Street; and worldwide interest was expressed. The New York Times listed him amongst the most outstanding inventors of the past 80 years. Meanwhile the scientific world continued to receive him rather coolly, and the battle to steal his thunder and keep him out of commercial television was beginning.

In 1927 Baird set up the Baird Television Development Company. He was a popular boss, seen as the entrepreneurial eccentric, and known as "Personality Joe" to his employees. But only one day after setting up his company, Bell Television in America announced the launch of their own station.

BAIRD AND THE BBC

The next few years saw intense creative activity on Baird's part, and successive ground-breaking feats. In 1929 Baird helped to set up a television company in Berlin – Fernseh AG. By this time the first programmes were also being transmitted from the newly formed British Broadcasting Corporation. Baird also succeeded in moving television into the open air, so dispensing with artificial light, and gave the first ever outdoor transmission on 8 May 1931. This led to one of his greatest achievements; the televising of the Derby. By experimenting with filters Baird also came up with colour television and later three-dimensional television. In 1931, after experimenting with television and telephones, Baird had produced "Phonovision" – the first portable television receiver.

THE WIFE EXPERIMENT

Being now well into his forties, Baird decided it was time to marry. He wanted a cultured, musical wife but had never found the time to go through the ususal elaborate sifting and courting ritual. With his usual flair for practical organization he overcame this problem by holding fake auditions for concert pianists. Baird watched from behind a curtain and appraised the contestants. As a result he married one Margaret Albu, and to the surprise of most people apart from himself, the marriage was a happy one.

THE STRUGGLE TO CONTROL TELEVISION

Meanwhile rivals were springing up all around Baird in the race for financial gain. There were repeated attempts to block Baird's power in the BBC and to hold up research funds. Undeterred, Baird set up his own television studios in order to investigate ultra-short waves. But events conspired against him: in the States his licence to broadcast was revoked; and the Second World War was to see an end to his involvement in Germany.

Then, in 1934, the inevitable showdown in Britain began: the Postmaster General announced a special commission to investigate the launch of high definition television to be run by the BBC. Trials were held between the two main contenders: Baird and EMI Marconi.

Baird's 240 line system was based on a mechanical scanning device. His research suffered setbacks and, it is now thought, almost certain sabotage. Eventually EMI won the deal since their system was electronic and scanned the picture with a moving beam of electrons. It had fewer lines and a greater range, and could therefore reach a larger audience. Baird was bitterly disappointed to be pushed out of the running, and he was never to regain the prominence he once had. His profile sank, the liquidation of the Baird Company followed in 1940, and once again Baird faced a lack of funds to continue his projects. The resentment stayed with Baird for the rest of his life.

"I feel again the anger against the jealous malice which would willingly, against all justice and evidence, have brushed my work aside."

COLOUR TELEVISION

In the following years Baird was far from inactive as many commentators have claimed. From 1941 he was technical adviser to Cable and Wireless Co. Ltd, and three years later he demonstrated the world's first all-electronic colour and three-dimensional receiver as well as facsimile television – a forerunner of Ceefax. In the same year Baird was recording and replaying typed material on cine film – he had discovered video.

NOCTOVISION AND RADAR

In 1926 Baird had demonstrated "Noctovision". The glare of hot lamps for lighting had led him to try infra-red, an effect he accomplished by covering the bulbs with thin ebonite. Infra-red allowed Baird to film in the dark.

Radar was a development of Noctovision. Though the exact extent of Baird's involvement in radar remains a mystery, he had a long-standing interest in detection systems. This was obviously of great secret strategic interest to the British government, and Baird was experimenting with systems comparable to radar as early as 1923.

Because of the intervening Second World War, the existence of radar was kept secret and not revealed by the press until 1941 as 'Radiolocation and Ranging'. Radio waves of an appropriate wavelength were transmitted out to be reflected from aeroplanes or ships. The reflected waves reached a receiver aerial which was usually combined with a transmitter aerial. A display screen showed the direction, distance and height of the reflected subjects. Radar has played a vital role in the military ever since its discovery and it seems more than likely that it was Baird who developed it for Britain in time for the war.

FIBRE OPTICS

There can be no doubt that Baird also pioneered the development of fibre optics: the transmission of light down bundles of very fine, optically insulated glass or plastic fibres. An undistorted image can be sent from one end to the other, enabling otherwise inaccessible parts of a machine or the human body to be inspected. The light may also be used to transmit data. It is a development which has proved invaluable in many areas of scientific research, especially in medicine.

BAIRD'S SIGNIFICANCE

Baird died at home one night in 1946, finally succumbing to the ill-health that had nagged him throughout his life. Without question he was a brilliant inventor and synthesizer – able to create vital links where others had failed. Great as his contribution to twentieth century technology has been, the full extent of his work remains unknown, wrapped in the classified secrecy of the Ministry of Defence.

CHAPTER XXII

(1863 – 1944)
LEO HENDRIK BAEKELAND

In our pollution-conscious society today, 'plastic' is associated with all that is artificial, cheap, and unpleasant for the evironment. The world actually just refers to a material which can be moulded or pressed into shape during some stage in its manufacture, and the first 'plastics' were even made of natural substances such as ivory and rubber.

SYNTHETICS

These first 'plastics' were naturally expensive, and with the rapid industrialisation of the world the need for machine casings and insulatory materials which were cheap and light, increased dramatically. Instead of looking around for naturally occurring products which would serve this purpose, scientists in the early nineteenth century discovered that they could build up familiar substances, from vinegar even to diamonds, by bringing together their constituent parts. This was named *synthesis* by the first scientist to have achieved this process, a Frenchman called Berthelot. Over the

years, however, "synthetic" substances came to be associated with the idea of cheap substitutes to the original product, rather than as man-made substances in themselves.

CELLULOID

There were many attempts to commercialise synthetic plastics – one of the greatest early successes was the invention of celluloid by the American John Hyatt. Celluloid was made from gun-cotton waste, castor oil and camphor, and made an excellent substitute for ivory in the making of billiard balls. It could be shaped easily when heated to 100°F, cut or drilled, and was very strong. When drawn out thinly it was also very flexible, and banished starched shirt collars almost overnight when strips were inserted into garments. The future photographic film magnate, George Eastman, founded his fortune on applying the discovery of celluloid to making the first flexible photographic film.

One of the problems with celluloid, apart from its

139

high flammability, was that it softened when heated, thereby restricting its uses. Several attempts were made to find a plastic that would not soften again once it had been cooled, and the first completely man-made plastic was eventually invented by a Belgian chemist in 1907, Leo Hendrik Baekeland.

THE BRILLIANT IMMIGRANT

Dr. Baekeland was a young, highly acclaimed professor of chemistry and physics in the university town of Gent in Belgium. In 1889 the Belgian government sent him to America to study institutes of higher education there, a trip which he combined with his honeymoon. While he was there he was offered a lucrative position at the Anthony Company (later to become ANSCO) which was the largest photgraphic firm in New York. As the industry of photography was still in its infancy there were many technical manufacturing problems which could only be solved at the time by consulting an outside chemist. Having Baekeland on the staff represented something of an innovation.

Two years later Baekeland left the company with the idea of setting up an experimental laboratory as a consultant chemist to American industries. This really was too radical for the times, and after a few years of desultory experiments and money losing projects, Baekeland realised he and his young family would be left penniless unless he focussed his energies soon.

VELOX

In Belgium at the age of twenty, Baekeland had experimented with an idea for a photographic paper which would be sensitive enough to be processed in artificial light. His two years with the Anthony Company made him realise the potential of this and he set out to perfect the process, which he called *Velox*. Together with a partner he set up the Napera Chemical Company to manufacture the paper, and in 1899 sold the patent and factory to George Eastman of the Eastman Kodak Company for a million dollars.

Baekeland was now thirty seven, and a millionaire. He was at last able to equip his laboratory and take his time over new research. First of all however, in 1906 he took his wife and young family on what must have been one of the earliest automobile tours in history. Baekeland piled his family and ten leather suitcases into a specially-built green leather-upholstered Peerless limousine, and jaunted off with them for months around France, England and Italy. On his return to America he wrote a delightful book about the experience: *A Family Motor Tour Through Europe.*

THE POLYMERS

Baekeland next applied himself to research into an artifical resin to replace the expenive *shellac*, a natural gum much in demand by the manufacturing industry for varnishing surfaces. What he was trying to create was an artificial *polymer*, a substance in which the fundamental molecule combines with itself over and over again in endless combinations. Natural polymers such as resin and amber already existed, but the only artifical polymer ever created by man was glass, invented by the Phoenicians 1500 years ago.

For over thirty years it had been known that the two simplest organic compounds, phenol (carbolic acid) and the water-soluble, reactive gas formaldehyde, would react in various ways when combined. When they were mixed together and heated, a thick brown substance resulted that was almost beyond chemical analysis. It hardened into a solid black sponge, a consistency achieved by the gas bubbles produced in the heated mixture. Because previous researchers into this mixture had tried to keep the bubbling to a minimum, the compounds were heated to the lowest possible temperature – well below that of boiling water.

THE DISCOVERY OF BAKELITE

Baekeland discovered that if he pumped air into the glass retort before applying heat to his compounds, the gas was unable to escape and all bubbling was blocked. Then, if the temperature of the mixture was raised to twice that of boiling water, the reaction was completed in a few minutes. He could also control the reaction by by adding dilute acid to the mixture, which would result in a thick, clear liquid. If he added alkaline substances the mixture would harden into a clear, hard mass which was insoluble and would not soften. The amount of acid would determine the pliability of this mixture, which could then be moulded before it hardened. After two more years of experimenting his substance was so perfected that it was heat resistant (unlike resins), would not corrode, or shrink after removal from its mould like

A 1912 advertisement extolling the novel virtues of Bakelite-laquered furniture. This was the beginning of a design revolution that gathered force through the 1920's and 1930's.

celluloid. It could also be machined to a precision almost as fine as brass. This extraordinary invention, now protected by four hundred patents, was christened *Bakelite*.

At first, Baekeland used his new substance to produce a subsitute for resin as a varnish. At a meeting in 1909 before the recently formed New York Chemists Club, he delightedly outlined the properties of his new varnish:

"It is very hard, cannot be scratched with the finger nail; in this respect it is far superior to shellac and even to rubber. It misses one great quality of hard rubber and celluloid, it is not so elastic nor flexible. As an insulator and for any purposes where it has to resist heat, friction, dampness, steam or chemicals, it is far superior to hard rubber, casein, celluloid, shellac, and in fact all plastics. In price it can also compare splendidly with these . . . I may simply dip an object into it or coat it by means of a brush, and provide it rapidly with a hard brilliant coat of Bakelite, superior to any varnish and even better than the most expensive Japanese lacquer."

THE BAKELISER

Cheaper than the most expensive Japanese lacquers the extraordinary new substance might have been, but to manufacture this plastic was still a risky and costly process. Baekeland had designed his own oven, the *Bakeliser* for his experiments, and set it up in a corner by his garage. To make the Bakelite go further he mixed it with inexpensive fillers, such as wood pulp, asbestos or chalk which also gave it extra strength. It was a great success, and Baekeland soon set up a factory in 1907 to expand manufacture.

Bakelite had new uses too. It proved to be an excellent electrical insulator, all of a sudden a desperate requirement as electricity began to network across the United States. The developers of radios, and the whole burgeoning automobile industry, seized on the new product with delight.

THE BAKELITE DESIGN

Soon it was not only the unglamorous hidden or unimportant visible components which were made out of the new material, including light switches and plugs which can still be found today, but a whole era of design began to be influenced by bakelite.

Because it was difficult to mould objects with sharp corners, Bakelite objects tended to have a rounded, streamlined shape. This became a characteristic of design in the nineteen thirties. Its colours were rather limited and uninteresting – black, dark brown or dark green – and before long new plastics were produced by replacing the phenol with urea. This resulted in a similar substance to bakelite, but translucent and colourless, which could be tinted in the pastel greens, pinks and yellows which proved to be so popular in the following decades. All of a sudden it was impossible to get away from Bakelite: everything from tables and radios to cereal bowls were manufactured, and are becoming collectors' items today.

THE PLASTICS INDUSTRY

After Bakelite and the urea formaldehye plastics the flood gates were opened, and hundreds of new plastics with different properties have been developed since.

Baekeland remained head of his Bakelite Corporation. He was given honours and awards: during the First World War he worked for the National Research Council, and was made President of the American Chemical Society in 1924. By 1930 his Bakelite Corporation had grown to cover a thirty acre site in New Jersey, and had absorbed several competitors.

He always remained a fun-loving, easy-going man, just as interested in camping with his children, sailing in his yacht and teaching all his grandchildren to cook before they reached the age of ten, as in heading his very profitable corporation. He died in 1944 just before the war ended. He was the first chemist in America to apply his science to industry in the most practical way, so that it was said that after the animal, vegetable and mineral kingdom, Baekeland had opened up the fourth, plastic kingdom. It was a vital legacy to the twentieth century – it would be impossible to live without plastics today. One irony that the genial Dr. Baekeland did not foresee was that the success of plastics is so total that it threatens to overwhelm an environment not yet geared up to disposing of them again.

Two Bakelite radios c. 1930. During the 1920's, the original range of brown and black Bakelite colours had been widely extended to include popular pastel shades.

CHAPTER XXIII

(1912 – 1954)
ALAN TURING

Most of the scientists and inventors included in this book are well known to the general public, at least as famous names. Considering the importance of computers in so many aspects of life today, Alan Turing and the other pioneers of this field have been surprisingly neglected. Yet his ideas had an important influence on the development of computers between the late 1940s and 1960s, and they are still widely respected in expert circles.

Several factors contributed to Turing's low profile with the public. When his interest in computers began, in the mid 1930's, he was far ahead of his time and the technology needed to put his ideas into practice did not yet exist. Electronics began to catch up with him during the second World War, but the vital work which he carried out on the breaking of enemy codes could not receive public recognition at that time. Another reason is that he did not fit easily into the society of his day as a person. He often expressed his ideas in a rather iconoclastic and sometimes deliberately provocative manner, and he was a lonely man who was rarely at his ease when working with others in an institution.

Dr Andrew Hodges, his biographer, sums up Turing's importance in this way.

"He was the first theoretician of the computer; he invented the idea of the computer in the mid-1930's. I do not mean that he was the first person to think about calculating machines, but he was the first to have the idea that a machine could do anything you tell it to do – like a computer which we can program any way we like."

LOOMS AND PIANOLAS

The idea of a machine that is capable of some flexibility of action, and which can be controlled by a set of instructions (a program), can be traced back nearly two hundred years. The French weaver Joseph Marie Jacquard (1752 – 1834) invented a loom which could be controlled by punched cards to weave patterns in silk automatically. It aroused bitter opposition from other weavers at first, but there were soon thousands of automatic looms in use throughout Europe. Jacquard's loom was the forerunner of many other kinds of automated machines. An example of a very different kind, the pianola, was a very popular form of home entertainment until it was overtaken by the development of the gramophone in the 1920s. These were also controlled by means of holes punched in card, and this piano roll, or program, gives quite precise control over the reproduction of the music. (The composer Percy Grainger was able to "perform" as the soloist at the last night of the BBC Promenade Concerts in 1988, by this means, nearly twenty years after his death).

BABBAGE'S "ANALYTICAL ENGINE"

A more direct ancestor of the twentieth century computer was invented by Charles Babbage (1792 – 1871), another rather neglected pioneer – and another man ahead of his time. His "engine" was more than just a complex calculating machine and its design included, in principle, many of the features which were to be incorporated into computers more than a century later. Babbage's main aim was to develop a means of producing mathematical tables mechanically, in order to reduce the errors which inevitably creep in if they are calculated and then copied out by a human being. Such tedious, repetitive and exact work is the ideal sort of task for a computer. He worked for many years on his "difference engine", which would not only calculate the figures but would also print them out directly. He tried to persuade the government that this project would be valuable for producing the accurate mathematical tables that were needed for navigation, and rather reluctantly they gave him some financial help.

While he was still building the "difference engine" his thoughts had already moved ahead to a far more sophisticated project, and he tried to obtain further money to develop this. When the government refused to increase his grant he completed the simpler version and set it to work in 1827 to calculate and print tables of logarithms.

Turing's prototype computer at the university of Manchester, in June 1948. The six central racks ran the world's first stored program. A year later it's capacity had doubled in size.

The more advanced project, which he called an "analytical engine", was intended to be far more adaptable. It was to be a machine capable of carrying out any required sequence of mathematical operations – like the later programmable computers, and the program, as in Jacquard's loom, was to be provided by a set of punched cards. The Royal Society recommended that the government should assist with this further development, but he never managed to persuade them that it was a realistic proposition and received no further financial help. This may in the long run have been less short-sighted than it seemed.

Babbage experienced great difficulty in getting the moving parts produced to the high degree of accuracy that would have been required. Also, a purely mechanical system would have been very slow in carrying out a complex series of operations, unlike later electronic computers. Like Turing a hundred years later, Babbage's ideas were too far ahead of the technology available at the time, and it is not certain that he could have produced a satisfactory working model even if he had managed to obtain more enthusiastic government support.

He continued working at the idea, using much of his private family money, until he was eventually forced to abandon it unfinished. One of Babbage's other projects was even less successful in financial terms. Together with the poet Lord Byron's daughter, who was an extremely gifted mathematician, he spent some time trying to work out a foolproof mathematical system for picking the winners in a horse race. No doubt as one of the great statisticians of his time, and the founder of the Statistical Society, he should have known better, and he lost a lot of money before giving up the idea!

THE TURING MACHINE

Alan Turing came to the study of computers by a different route. At first he was not concerned with the possibility of actually making a practical machine, but as a brilliant young mathematician at Cambridge, he was more interested in solving some rather abstract theoretical problems. For example, some mathematicians held that the whole of mathematics could be built up from sets of axioms and the theorems derived from these, following the tradition of Euclid's geometry. Others claimed that there were some aspects of mathematics

Turing with two engineers from Ferranti at his computer in 1951.

which could not be built up in this way. Turing devised a novel way of thinking about such propositions. He imagined a machine which would have an unlimited paper tape containing instructions in the form of symbols that it could read and respond to – and to which it could write the results of processing these instructions.

When he put forward this idea in 1937 there seemed to be no prospect of ever actually building a "Turing machine", but it provided a highly original and successful means of solving the theoretical problems that he was concerned with. By using the idea of this hypothetical machine he was able to demonstrate that there is no purely routine or mechanical procedure which can decide whether a given mathematical proposition could be derived from a set of axioms. But, almost as an unintended side-product of these ideas, he had also outlined all the main features which would eventually form a modern computer, and had foreseen some of the ways that such a system could be applied.

DECIPHERING THE ENIGMA

During the Second World War his talents were put to an important practical use with the British code breaking organisation at Bletchley Park. Here he helped to develop an electronic device and supplied the sophisticated ideas in mathematics and logic that were required

Windows

Rotors

Plugboard

Light sockets

for deciphering the output of the German "enigma" code machine. For the first time he was working with electronic equipment which had some of the capabilities of his imaginary machines. Under the pressures of war, electronics was making very rapid progress and it began to be possible to consider building a working computer. While the war continued Turing remained mainly concerned with code breaking, and for some time had responsibility for deciphering communications between the U-boats in the Atlantic and their bases. The vital information which was obtained saved many ships and hundreds of lives, and it probably altered the whole course of the war at sea. In his book "The Physicists", C.P. Snow says that the almost unknown Turing . . . "did more practical service to the country than could be credited to most household names of that war".

After the war many groups in Britain and America began to take advantage of the improvements in electronics to build the first generation of computers. There was much cross-fertilisation of ideas and it is difficult to apportion the credit to individuals. Alan Turing was involved in designing what would have been one of the most advanced of these early computers – "ACE", the Automatic Computing Engine, which was to be installed at the National Physical Laboratory. But he became increasingly frustrated as the project became bogged down in bureaucratic delays and disputes over costs, and eventually he accepted a post at the University of Manchester where he could work on a computer which was much less powerful, but was actually working. During this period, in the late 1940s, he also started working on another completely original field, mathematical biology, in which he used mathematics to study the patterns of growth and development in plants and animals.

ELECTRONIC BRAINS

Turing believed that a computer could be programmed to imitate the working of the human mind and that this, in turn, would throw new light on the working of human intelligence. He saw logical similarities between the way the human brain processes information and the operations of an electronic computer. He talked about computers as "electronic brains" and believed that, in theory, a machine could do anything the human brain can do. He explained his views in lectures, newspaper interviews and private conversations. These ideas were expressed most completely in his paper "Computing Machinery and Intelligence", which was published in 1950 in the journal Mind. This work had a great influence on the still infant field of computer science, which was by then beginning to develop rapidly. In particular it was one of the main foundations of what has come to be called artificial intelligence.

The Turing Institute in Glasgow is a centre for present day research in artificial intelligence, and Professor Michie says that in some ways the Institute is still catching up with ideas that Alan Turing outlined forty years ago:

"The idea of simulating human thought processes and human knowledge was in Turing's mind from the start. By the time that I knew him he foresaw, and considered the most important project of all to be, the possibility of developing not only numerical calculating power in computers but reasoning, associative memory and learning. These are the useful mental skills that, until now, we have had to rely entirely on human beings to perform."

FINAL FRUSTRATION

Turing predicted, and influenced, many of the developments which have later come to pass in computing, such as the importance of information technology, the possibility of linking computers into networks and ways for humans and machines to interact with each other. To the end he was full of stimulating ideas, but he had very little talent for diplomacy or for the political manoevering which takes place in any institution. By the early 1950s he was playing a rather low-key role in the development of programming techniques, and he was feeling increasingly dissatisfied and frustrated by the intellectual limitations of his work. Then he was suddenly plunged into a personal crisis. He had always been quite open about being homosexual, even though at this period it was still a criminal offence in Britain. In 1954 he was dragged through the courts, convicted, and subjected to hormone therapy.

In the June of that year he was found dead at his home near Manchester, having apparently committed suicide by taking cyanide. And so the world lost, at the age of forty-one, one of the most brilliant and visionary pioneers of computer science.

CHAPTER XXIV

(1874 – 1955)
ALBERT EINSTEIN

Albert Einstein stands with Newton, high above the other great names of science. He became an international figure when his theory of Relativity dazzled – and bewildered – the world seventy years ago, and still today his face is instantly recognisable by many of the general public, although his ideas seem remote from everyday experience. In fact he is often seen almost as a symbol of the incomprehensible genius. Reflecting this feeling, J.C. Squire answered Pope's epitaph for Isaac Newton:

> Nature, and Nature's laws lay hid in night:
> God said, 'Let Newton be!' and all was light.
> It did not last: the devil roaring 'Ho!
> Let Einstein be!" restored the status quo.

Einstein, like Newton, asked new questions about things that seemed familiar, but his brilliantly simple questions gave unfamiliar answers which have radically changed our ideas about the world. The importance of these ideas was later underlined, to his and the world's anguish, by the immense dilemmas that face the human race as a result of the increased power over nature that he and the other creators of twentieth century science have given us. Einstein himself was caught up by many of the tragic issues of his time: the persecution of the Jews, the violence of war and the development of nuclear weapons. His passionate belief in social justice and non-violence, as well as his humour and modesty, ensure that he will be remembered not only as a genius, but as a great and good man.

THE PATENT OFFICER

Einstein was born in Württemberg, in Germany. His father was a chemical engineer, but his business forced the family to move several times and this disrupted the young Albert's education. At seventeen he entered college in Zürich – after some delays because of his low standard in mathematics. When he graduated in 1901 he hoped to become a teacher but because he was a Jew it was impossible for him to find a post, so he took a junior position at the Patent Office in Berne.

At this time he was also carrying out research for his doctorate and he continued to keep in touch, as far as he could, with the exciting developments then taking place in science. During the next few years he published a few papers, although these gave little hint of what was to come. Then in 1905/6, at the age of twenty six, came three great publications which stunned the scientific world.

Such a man could no longer be ignored and he was at last offered a teaching post at the University of Berne. Four years later he became professor of physics at Zürich, then at the University of Prague. In 1913 he moved to Berlin, on being made a member of the Royal Prussian Academy of Sciences, and he remained there until the winter of 1932 when he visited America, a visit which was to become a permanent stay.

BROWNIAN MOTION

In the least well known of his 1905 papers he demonstrated his clear scientific vision by clearing up a niggling loose end. In 1828 the English botanist Robert Brown (1773-1858), while he was observing pollen under a microscope, noticed that the tiny grains were continually moving with small random jerks. Neither he nor anyone else could find any explanation. "Brownian Motion" remained a minor mystery until Einstein realised that the molecules of the water, in which the pollen was floating, were colliding with the pollen grains. The grains are so light that the effect of these collisions can be seen, even though the water molecules themselves are far too small to be seen even under the most powerful microscope.

Surprisingly, this was the first experimental evidence for the existence of molecules. Even in 1905 some influential scientists (for example, Ernst Mach) still refused to accept the atomic theory, in the absence of evidence that confirmed it. Sadly, it was in this year that

Einstein in front of blackboard calculations of his Relativity theory.

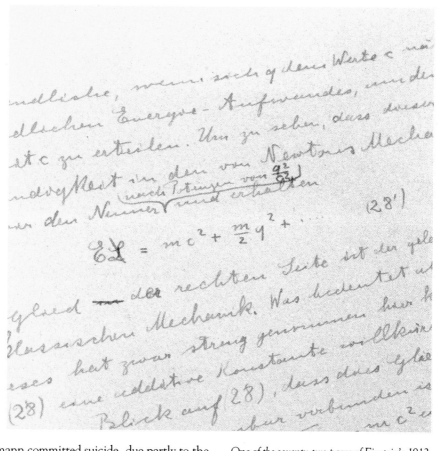

One of the seventy-two pages of Einstein's 1912 manuscript, setting out his theory of Relativity.

Ludwig Boltzmann committed suicide, due partly to the depression caused when many of his colleagues refused, on these grounds, to accept his important work on the kinetic theory of gases.

Einstein received his PhD in January 1906, but by then academic qualifications were superfluous. His other two papers, on Quantum theory and the theory of Relativity, had ensured him a permanent place in history.

WAVES OR PARTICLES?

His second paper of 1905 returned to the nature of light, a problem which already seemed to have been settled once and for all.

Newton had favoured the idea that light is a stream of corpuscles, while others regarded it as a wave motion in an "ether". Either view could explain what was known about light in the eighteenth century, but Newton's immense reputation tipped the balance for most scientists at first. Thomas Young (1773-1829) realised that he might be able to settle the question by experiment.

When any waves, including ripples on water, meet an obstruction which has small slits in it, the waves re-form after passing through the slits, and affect each other. Where two crests come together they reinforce each other, producing areas where the waves are stronger than before; but where a crest meets a trough they cancel each other out. If light is a wave motion it should show these interference effects as bands of light and dark on a screen placed beyond the slits – but this will not happen if light is a stream of particles.

This crucial experiment was carried out early in the

nineteenth century. When Young passed light through two narrow slits he found that it did indeed give interference effects. His results were confirmed in a similar experiment by Augustin Fresnel. It was easier for the French scientist to gain acceptance for this new evidence – Young had to argue against the national monument of Newton. But the dispute had at last been settled and the wave theory was victorious. It was later crowned by the work of James Clerk Maxwell (Chapter VI). Yet in his 1905 paper Einstein re-opened the whole question and provided a striking confirmation of the new Quantum theory.

THE QUANTUM THEORY

A problem had arisen in the 1890s on the way hot bodies radiate energy. For longer wavelengths the theory agreed well with experiment, but the calculations went very badly wrong for shorter wavelengths. A theory cannot be half right and many physicists tried to find a way out of this scientific embarrassment which became known as "the ultraviolet catastrophe".

Max Planck (1858-1947) struggled with the problem for five years until he found a solution which he published in 1900. He could get the calculations in line with the experimental evidence if light is given out, not continuously, but in small bursts – quanta. This is summed up by one of the two famous, if deceptively simple, equations of twentieth century science:

$$E = h\nu$$

(E is the amount of energy in one of these packets of light and ν, the Greek letter nu, represents the frequency of the light. They are linked together by "Planck's constant", h)

To most scientists, perhaps even to Planck, this at first seemed little more than a mathematical trick. Einstein, however, saw that if it was taken literally it explained a puzzling feature of the photo-electric effect. This happens when light shines on certain materials and produces electricity by knocking electrons out of their atoms. There are several useful applications of this, for example in television cameras, light meters and solar cells.

The problem was that light of short wavelengths (blue or violet) knocks out some electrons even if it is dim, yet red light (of long wavelength) produces nothing, even if it is very bright. It was as though breakers leave a sandcastle untouched as long as they are widely spaced, but even small ripples occasionally knock chunks out of it, provided they are close together. Einstein realised that light is not behaving like waves here, but like Newton's corpuscles.

He showed that Planck's quanta was not just an oddity in the way atoms give out radiation, but that light itself can only exist in small packets, or photons. The energy of an individual photon depends on the frequency of the light, as in Planck's equation. This explained why light of long wavelengths (low frequency) produces no photo-electric effect: the individual photons do not have enough energy to knock out an electron when they hit an atom. But the high energy photons of violet light will knock out an electron. If the light is dim there are few of them, but each photon packs a greater punch.

It was in essence a simple idea, but it takes us into deep waters. It revived the particle theory, yet it still involves a wavelength: the two contradictory ideas are now firmly tied together. It was no longer a question of which is right: both are needed to explain light, even though we cannot visualise something which has two

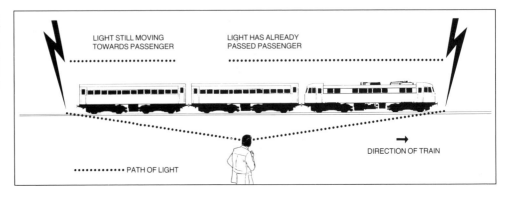

The "thought experiment" of Einstein's to illustrate the relativity of speed and time (see page 154).

LIGHT STILL MOVING TOWARDS PASSENGER

LIGHT HAS ALREADY PASSED PASSENGER

DIRECTION OF TRAIN

PATH OF LIGHT

Albert Einstein with the English Prime Minister, Ramsay Macdonald in Berlin in 1931. To the left of Macdonald is Professor Max Planck, the German physicist.

apparently mutually exclusive characteristics.

Einstein was unable to accept the profound implications of the Quantum theory, even though he may be considered its co-founder. He was particularly uneasy about one of its consequences, the "Uncertainty Principle", stated by Werner Heisenberg in 1923. This reveals a built-in limitation to the amount of information that it is possible to have about the world. For example, we may know that a particular electron has a certain amount of energy, but we cannot know exactly where it will turn up: it does not act like a well-behaved snooker ball, as even the smallest objects should do in Newton's view of the world. As we home in on the fine detail of nature, reality becomes fuzzy – rather as a newspaper picture becomes when we look at it very closely.

Einstein could not accept a world ultimately determined by probabilities. He felt, in his famous phrase, that: "God does not play dice with the world". (In a moment of friendly irritation Niels Bohr once told Einstein "Stop telling God what to do!") To the end of his life he tried to find some way out of this, but never

succeeded; at the most basic levels of the universe it seems that God really does play dice. Despite these misgivings, it was for this work, rather than Relativity, that he received the Nobel prize in 1922.

THE THEORY OF RELATIVITY

Einstein's most famous work again arose from his ability to ask profoundly simple questions, and to follow his thoughts through wherever they took him. The first stirrings of the theory came when, as a boy of fourteen, he wondered what the world would look like if he could ride on a beam of light. But the formal starting point was another tiresome problem that surfaced towards the end of the last century, this time concerning the velocity of light. By hindsight it was another warning that Newton's "majestic clockwork" was about to break down.

Maxwell's theory (Chapter VI) implied that light has a particular velocity, but the puzzling thing was that the velocity seemed to remain constant, irrespective of the movement of the observer or the light source. This seems to go against commonsense. For example, if I am cycling at 10 m.p.h. and the wind is blowing from the opposite direction at 15 m.p.h. I have to battle against a 25 m.p.h. wind. Those lucky enough to be cycling in the same direction as the wind only feel a breeze of 5 m.p.h. The same sort of calculation works in any other normal circumstances; it seemed impossible that light could be different: if we cycle towards a lamp, surely its light must reach us at a greater speed than if we were moving away from it?

In 1886 in the United States, Albert Michelson and Edward Morley devised an accurate experiment to measure the velocity of light. They hoped to use their new apparatus to discover how fast the earth is moving, by measuring the velocity of light in different directions and comparing these different velocities, much like our example of cycling against the wind. They were surprised to find that there was no difference: light travelled at the same speed, whether it was going with or against the movement of the earth.

Once they were certain the apparatus was reliable, various scientists tried to explain this odd result. Some suggested that a pocket of "ether" got caught up by the earth and travelled along with it. Others tinkered with the mathematics, notably the Dutch physicist Hendrik Lorentz (1853-1928). His modification to the equations required that objects shrink as they move. At low speeds the effect is negligible but the shrinking becomes greater as the velocity approaches that of light. This balanced the books but, like Planck's original statement of the Quantum theory, it seemed to be little more than a mathematical trick and it gave no insight into why such a contraction might happen.

THE MESSENGER OF THE UNIVERSE

These ideas came together in Einstein's mind with another apparently simple problem: how to measure the speed of light from one point to another? He came to the conclusion that this is just not possible. Once the light signal has left its starting point you cannot contact the other end before it arrives. You always have to time the two way journey, from when the light signal leaves its starting point until you see it reflected back again. Light is the ultimate messenger of the universe.

In one of his famous "thought experiments" Einstein considered what would be seen if lightning struck twice along the track of a moving train, one stroke in front of the train the other an equal distance behind it. Suppose

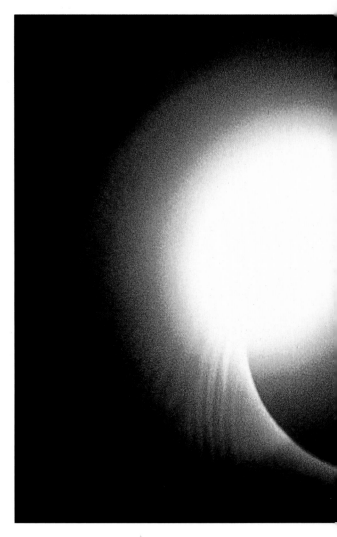

an observer, who is standing on the bank next to the track, sees these two lightning strokes happen simultaneously; will a man in the train agree?

Einstein's answer is no. The light from both flashes travels towards the man in the train at the same speed. It will take longer for the flash from behind to reach him, because the train is continuing to move forward while the light is travelling towards him. The opposite will be true for the flash seen ahead. So for the man on the train the two flashes are not simultaneous. If the man on the bank insists that HE must be right because he was standing still, the train passenger would point out that he certainly is not stationary either. He is travelling around

A total solar eclipse taken in June 1983, showing the "diamond ring" effect. The fainter blue around the edge of the moon's disc is the solar corona, the sun's outer atmosphere. In 1919 Einstein proved that during a total eclipse light from stars could be seen to bend as it passed close to a massive body such as the sun – due to the warping of space-time.

Einstein's theory predicts that they will have very different time scales; the same considerations apply equally to all the other measurable quantities of nature, such as distance or mass. None of these can any longer be regarded as absolute quantities.

In the extreme case imagined by the fourteen year old Einstein, if the train was travelling at the speed of light relative to the bank, the passenger would never know that lightning had struck behind him because the light could never overtake the train – nor could any message from the man on the bank reach him. Time in the world outside the train would have stopped: so according to Einstein the speed of light is the ultimate natural speed limit.

In another stroke of genius Einstein showed that his theory leads to a merger between two quantities that had seemed to be entirely separate. The mass and energy content of a body are linked together by that other, and even more famous, equation of the twentieth century, which implies that a vast amount of energy would be released if a small amount of mass can be destroyed:

$$E = MC^2$$

This is all very different from the world as Newton saw it: he assumed that time rolls along at its own pace, and that mass and space are quite unaffected by where you are, or how you are moving. Maybe from God's viewpoint there are such things as absolute space and time but according to Einstein all of us who are part of the universe carry our own space-time with us.

Einstein completed his theory in 1915 with the publication of the General Theory. Just as the Special Theory of 1905 had altered Newton's laws of mechanics, the General Theory was a new way of looking at the working of gravity. Einstein talked of space and time together as four dimensions, and said that the presence of matter warped the fabric of space-time itself. Instead

as the earth spins, and travelling along with the earth and the sun as they move through space.

The only way to settle the argument would be to ask an umpire who is standing somewhere that is ABSOLU-TELY stationary: but since we no longer believe in the crystalline spheres of medieval astronomy, there is no such special place in the entire universe. Light is the ultimate messenger, so Einstein's two observers must agree to differ.

Of course, in the normal world the speed of the train is so slow, compared with the speed of light, that the difference between their view-points is too small to measure. But if their relative speeds are large, then of a planet being kept in its orbit by the force of gravity pulling it towards the sun, as in Newton's theory, Einstein said that the mass of the sun distorts the space around it and because of this space-warp the planet moves in a new path.

RELATIVITY PUT TO THE TEST

This was all so revolutionary that, no matter how impeccable the logic appeared to be, many refused to accept the theory. After all, so far there was no proof for any of it. Most of the possible tests were beyond the technology of 1915, but there was one prediction that could be tested and might settle the doubts – if it were confirmed.

According to Relativity the light from a distant star will bend if it passes close to a massive body such as the sun, due to the warping of space. Normally the sun blots out the light from the stars during the day, but during a total eclipse it should be possible to detect slight shifts in the expected positions of stars near the sun in the sky. In 1918, Einstein took the opportunity of a solar eclipse due in May 1919 to ask for his ideas to be tested. Although the First World War was still in progress, the Royal Society and the Royal Astronomical Society agreed. In his book "Relativity, A Popular Exposition" of 1920, Einstein comments on the results:

"Undaunted by difficulties of both a material and psychological nature caused by the war, the Societies equipped two expeditions – to Brazil and to the island of Principe (West Africa) – and sent several of Britain's most celebrated astronomers . . . The results confirmed the theory in a thoroughly satisfactory manner."

The idea of starlight bending, and the extravagant nature of the test, caught the popular imagination and the theory became news – not just in scientific circles, but in the world's press. The fact that Relativity seemed too complicated even for many scientists to understand, if anything, helped to increase Einstein's popular reputation as a genius.

Since then relativity has been tested more thoroughly than any other theory, and even its most bizarre predictions have been bourne out. Once accurate enough clocks became available it was even possible to prove directly that time really does pass slower for someone who is moving, although only by millionths of a second at normal speeds, by carrying a very accurate atomic clock in an aircraft and comparing the time elapsed with that on a similar clock that did not move. If an object is massive enough any light trying to escape from it would bend back and never be able to leave. In effect space would have closed up on itself and the object would be out of contact with the rest of the universe: a black hole where, as far as outside observers are concerned, time and space have come to an end. This fantastic idea, too, has been confirmed by astronomers. And the conversion of matter into energy, predicted in his famous equation, explained how the stars produce their light. The terrible demonstration of this equation through nuclear weapons was yet to come.

AFTER RELATIVITY

By a fortunate chance Einstein arranged to visit the California Institute of Technology during the winter of 1932. When Hitler came to power in the following January he decided not to return to Germany and he took American citizenship. Einstein had himself suffered from antisemitism and he now became a prominent spokeman for the Jewish cause, helping many of the refugees who were streaming out of Germany. Like other scientists he became terrified that the Nazis might produce an atomic bomb and, despite his life-long pacifism, he wrote to President Roosevelt in 1939 urging that America should produce this weapon first, as a form of insurance. However, he was deeply disturbed when the bomb was used, without prior warning, at Hiroshima and Nagasaki, and after the war he tried to persuade the government not to go ahead with the development of thermonuclear weapons.

Einstein was a unique person who aroused affection as much as awe; he was a shy, humorous, approachable man, a lover of music and a keen violinist. He fitted popular ideas of what a great genius should be like and even looked the part, especially in later years, with his great mane of white hair and unconventional clothes. In his last years he grew apart from other scientists, both because of his refusal to accept the Quantum theory, and because he was absorbed in what proved to be a fruitless quest, to combine all the forces of nature into one grand unified theory. This is still the ultimate goal of science, and by the end of the century it begins to look possible. But any future development in our understanding of the universe will be built on the foundations Einstein laid.

CHAPTER XXV

(1871 – 1937)
ERNEST RUTHERFORD

The great revolution in our understanding of nature which began at the turn of the century is associated in many peoples minds mainly with the theoretical genius of men like Bohr, and especially Einstein; but the new foundations depended just as much upon the insight and practical skills of people like the Ernest Rutherford or the Curies. Lord Rutherford of Nelson, as he was to become, was one of the greatest experimental scientists of the twentieth century and by his own work, and the work of his associates and students, he firmly established the the science of nuclear physics.

THE COLONIAL

He was a big man in every sense, but tended to disguise his incisive mind behind a hearty, down-to-earth manner, which was almost a caricature of the no-nonsense colonial. Rutherford was a New Zealander, the son of Scottish immigrants. His father, James Rutherford, was a wheelwright and Ernest was brought up, with his ten brothers and sisters, on a small farm near Christchurch. It was in no way a privileged childhood, but he received a sound education at the local school and then in the college at Nelson. He later made brilliant progress at University and in 1895 was awarded a scholarship to to do research in Cambridge under Sir J.J. Thompson.

In his first year at Cambridge he carried out some of the early work on radio waves, for example he was able to detect effects over a distance of a kilometre, a remarkable achievement at that time. In 1896 he worked on the newly discovered X-rays which were exciting the whole of the scientific world. In the following year he began what was to occupy him for the rest of his life: the investigation of radioactivity. In 1898, while he was in the early stages of this work, he was appointed professor of physics at McGill University and moved to Montreal in Canada. There he began a very fruitful collaboration with Frederick Soddy (1877-1956), which was to be marked by the award of a Nobel Prize in 1908.

SOLID, MASSY AND HARD

In the first decade of the nineteenth century John Dalton (1766-1844) put forward his atomic theory, and so completed Lavoisier's foundation of the new science of chemistry. The idea behind the atomic theory had originated in the fifth century B.C. with the speculations of Leucippus and later Greek philosophers such as Democritus. Below the surface of a world of ceaseless change they held that all things consist of invisibly small, unchanging particles moving in the void ("at the heart of matter there is both plenitude and vacancy").

Dalton was able to apply the idea of the combination of atoms to explain the patterns which he found in the changes of mass that accompany chemical reactions. This led on to a comparison of the masses of the atoms of different elements, and he drew up the first tables of their "atomic weights". In 1869 the Russian chemist, Dmitri Mendeleyev, used atomic weights as the basis for his Periodic Table, bringing order and a remarkable natural pattern to the classification of the elements.

The atomic theory proved to be increasingly fruitful during the nineteenth century, although the atoms themselves were considered to be almost entirely beyond the reach of scientific investigation (and for this reason a few scientists refused to accept atoms as real). Up to the last few years of the nineteeth century the view of most scientists could still be summed up in the splendid words of Isaac Newton in the "Optiks":

"God in the beginning formed matter in solid, massy, hard, impenetrable, movable particles . . . even so hard as never to wear or break into pieces; no ordinary power being able to divide what God himself made one in the first creation".

Just as the atoms were indivisible, so the chemical elements were incapable of being decomposed. The idea of the transmutation of the elements had been rejected, along with the other pre-scientific ideas of alchemy, even before Lavoisier had published "The Elements of Chemistry". It is true that Faraday intuitively felt that science had not yet reached the final boundaries of matter. He even went so far as to say to William Crookes (who had discovered thallium):

"To discover a new element is a very fine thing, but if you could decompose an element and tell us what it is made of – that would indeed be a discovery worth making".

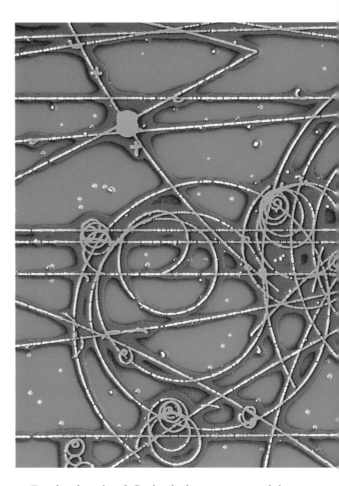

Faraday shared with Rutherford an instinctive ability to cut through the apparent complexity of things to an underlying simplicity, but most scientists would have regarded the idea of decomposing an element as wild, unscientific speculation.

BEYOND KNOWN FORCES

Rutherford's first major discovery about radioactivity was that at least two different forms of radiation were being given off; he called these alpha and beta rays. He showed that beta rays were streams of very fast moving, negatively charged particles, and were the same as the recently discovered electrons.

With Frederick Soddy he showed that radioactivity ".. is not affected by the most drastic chemical and physical treatment". In their paper of 1902 they go on to say:

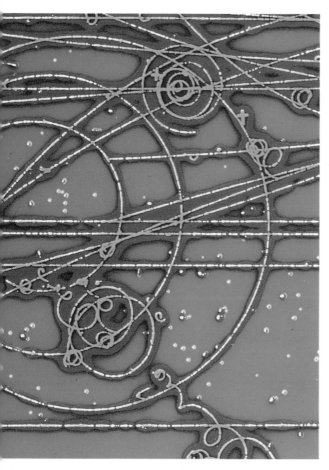

A 'false colour' photograph of the tracks of sub-atomic particles taken at the Cern laboratory in Geneva, 1989.

"Since, therefore, radioactivity is at once an atomic phenomenon and accompanied by chemical changes in which new types of matter are produced, these changes must be occurring within the atom and the radioactive elements must be undergoing spontaneous transformation . . . It is apparent that we are dealing with phenomena outside the sphere of known atomic forces".

In that one paragraph they demolished two of the greatest pillars of nineteenth century science. Rutherford went on to study alpha radiation in more detail and found that, like beta rays, it was a stream of particles shot out from the uranium atoms. He found that the alpha particles are identical to helium atoms, but carried a positive charge. By the time he left Montreal in 1907, to take up the chair of physics at Manchester University in England, they had proved conclusively that radioactivity involved the transmutation of one element into another

– and that the "solid, massy, hard" atoms were spontaneously breaking into pieces.

Rutherford might have agreed with Lord Kelvin, who once said that all science is "either physics or stamp collecting": he certainly considered himself a physicist. It therefore appealed to his sense of humour that when his work with Frederick Soddy was honoured by the award of a Nobel Prize in 1908 – it was for chemistry. He joked about his own spontaneous transmutation from physicist to chemist.

INSIDE THE ATOM

J.J. Thompson's discovery of the electron in 1897 had presented the scientific world with a considerable problem. Electrons had a negative charge and were only about a two-thousandth of the mass of hydrogen atoms – yet hydrogen were supposed to be the simplest form of matter. Furthermore, identical particles seemed to be produced from their atoms, whichever element he tested. It therefore appeared that electrons must, in some way, be a component part of all atoms. But if atoms were not simple particles it was very difficult to imagine what sort of structure they might have, or how such a minute object could ever be investigated.

Thompson put forward what came to be called the "currant bun" model of the atom; he imagined it as a ball of positively charged matter in which the electrons were embedded, like the currents in a bun. Atoms could therefore no longer be regarded as absolutely simple and featureless, but they were still imagined to be solid lumps of matter.

In Manchester Rutherford continued his investigation of radioactivity and he saw that the fast-moving alpha particles, which were nearly eight thousand times more massive than beta particles, might serve as useful probes in trying to gain more information about the atom. He set two of his students, Hans Geiger and Ernest Marsden, what appeared to be a fairly routine research project, to investigate how alpha particles are scattered when they strike a thin piece of gold foil. The results

Rutherford (with the cigarette) and his colleague John Ratcliffe at the Cavendish laboratory in Cambridge. The photographer mischievously posed Rutherford under a "Talk Softly Please!" sign – Rutherford was well-known for his booming voice.

they obtained did not seem to make any sense at all.

The great majority of the alpha particles passed straight through the gold with little or no deflection. This was strange enough, because even the thinnest piece of gold foil consists of many billions of atoms closely packed together, but the alpha particles were passing through all of them, almost as though the gold atoms were not there. It might be possible to explain this, but if so what seemed almost incredible was that about one in every 20,000 alpha particles behaved in an entirely different way and bounced back from the foil. Rutherford said that it was as though you fired artillary

shells at a sheet of tissue paper and found that some of them bounced back and hit you!

Eventually he realised that this had revealed something very important about the structure of atoms and, in the more sober language of his paper of 1911, he announced his conclusion:

"the structure assumed for the atom does not admit of a very large deflection of an alpha-particle . . . unless it be supposed that the sphere of positive electricity is minute compared with the diameter of the sphere of action of the atom".

His radically new picture of the atom was that almost the entire mass was concentrated into a minute central region, far smaller than the atom itself, and this nucleus carried a positive charge. The positive charge of the nucleus was balanced by an equal number of the even more minute electrons moving rapidly around it, rather like the sun with its planetary system. Since the atom is almost entirely empty space, the great majority of his alpha-particle probes passed straight through the gold atoms and it was only those which happened to approach close to the nucleus which were strongly affected.

Atoms themselves are so small, compared with even the smallest things we can see under a microscope, that it is almost impossible to visualise them. But on Rutherford's model the particles making up the atom are very much smaller still. If an atom were magnified to the size of a football stadium the nucleus would be only about the size of a golf ball, at the centre of the stadium, with a few flies buzzing around very rapidly, tracing out the rest of the space. Or in mathematical terms, the nucleus is about 10^{-15} metres in size, embedded in an electron cloud about 10^{-10} metres in diameter.

NEILS BOHR (1885-1962)

Rutherford affected to distrust theoreticians; he relied on his experimental skills and on a remarkable ability to cut through to the heart of a problem as his alpha particles cut through the atoms. But a very serious problem still remained about his model of the atom; his instincts told him that his interpretation of the evidence had to be right, yet it was equally clear that it conflicted with the well established laws of physics. If the negatively charged electrons really were moving rapidy around the nucleus they should be giving out radiation like any other moving charge. This is how radio waves are produced, by making an electric charge move up and down an aerial. But if the electrons radiated away energy they would slow down and spiral in to the nucleus. An atom that behaved like this would collapse in a fraction of a second – it just cannot be like a minature solar system. He had provided the data, but an escape from this contradiction had to be provided by the theoreticians, and the first successful solution came in 1913 from one of his most brilliant students.

The Danish scientist Neils Bohr (1885-1962) was in many ways a complete contrast to Rutherford. He was certainly not noted for his practical skills – it was said that he only had to be in the same town for other people's experiments to go wrong. When Neils Bohr had completed his doctorate in 1911 he went to work at first with J.J. Thompson in Cambridge. But he was not happy there and moved up to Manchester to join Rutherford's group. Despite the contrast between the rather shy and diffident young Dane and the rather overbearing Rutherford, they got on very well.

Bohr's theory of the atom brought together Rutherford's "solar system" model and the Quantum theory (Chapter XXIV). According to this, light and other forms of radiation are only given out or absorbed in multiples of a minimum amount – as quanta or photons. In that case energy could not just "leak away" gradually while an electron moves around the nucleus: it is all or nothing. The electron either continues to move in a stable path, or it gives out a complete quantum and jumps to a new path. This patched up the problems of Rutherford's atom brilliantly, and it also illuminated several other areas which until then had no satisfactory explanation. Most notably it accounted for the spectrum of the elements, their optical fingerprints which allow astronomers to identify the composition of the stars. It also gave, at last, an explanation of how atoms link together to form molecules (and began to bring chemistry within the fold of physics). It was one of those strokes of inspiration which fuse together ideas that seemed to be entirely unconnected but which afterwards seem to be natural, almost obvious, partners.

It was, however, a halfway house and had to give way to still more radical concepts during the following two decades. Neils Bohr remained at the forefront of most of these later theoretical developments.

SPLITTING THE ATOM

In 1914 Rutherford received a knighthood, then in 1919 he succeeded J.J. Thompson at Cambridge and over the next decade the Cavendish laboratory became the world's leading centre for experimental physics. It was here that he carried out the first artificial transmutation of one element into another. Once again he used alpha

The room in the Cavendish laboratory in Cambridge where James Chadwick, one of Rutherford's research team, discovered the power of the split atom in 1932.

particles as high energy projectiles, but in this case they were made to collide with the nuclei of lighter atoms such as nitrogen. When the alpha particles made a direct hit they were absorbed by the nucleus of the nitrogen atom and transformed it to an atom of oxygen. In the process another particle was released – Rutherford identified these as the positively charged building blocks of the nucleus, and called them protons.

He suggested that there might be a third particle in the atom, similar in mass to the protons but carrying no electric charge. In 1932 James Chadwick, one of his team at the Cavendish laboratory found such a particle – the neutron. In the same year Cockcroft and Walton used a high voltage accelerator to produce a beam of fast-moving protons with which they bombarded the nuclei of lithium atoms. This caused the disintegration of the nuclei – "splitting the atom".

This was not yet the era of "big physics", though. The science writer Ritchie Calder described a guided tour of the laboratory in that year.

"Abruptly, Rutherford said 'Do you want to see how it's done?' He put on his hat and, whistling, he led me to the high voltage lab. It was a darkened room; man-made lightning crackled and flashed . . . then came a clicking sound as a counter began to clock in the fragments of the splitting atoms. This fantastic machine, this atom-smasher, had been built by under Rutherford's inspiration by his two young men, Cockcroft and Walton. Compared with the high voltage accelerators of today it was engagingly primitive. In the true tradition of string and sealing-wax experimenters Rutherford's young men had used biscuit tins, plasticine and, I suspect, sugar crates."

Although Rutherford saw a positive virtue in this sort of improvisation, it was partly forced upon him by lack of funds. He is quoted as saying: "We haven't the money, so we've got to think." (In the picture, the sign above Rutherford's head was a joking reference to his booming voice, which researchers complained upset their delicate apparatus).

This rather ramshackle, if brilliantly improvised "atom smasher" was the direct ancestor of the huge accelerator at CERN, which continues the same quest to probe the ultimate nature of matter. But today vastly more power is required to "split" not the atom but the particles which are the building blocks of atoms, in order to reveal the still smaller and perhaps ultimate components of matter, the quarks.

Rutherford took pride in the simplicity not just of his apparatus, but of his whole approach to science.

"If we knew more about the nucleus we would find it is a much simpler thing than we suppose. These fundamental things I think have got to be simple. It is the non-fundamental things that are very complex. I am always a believer in simplicity, being a simple person myself".

But it took a man of no ordinary power to split "what God had made one in his original creation". The Cavendish laboratory under his leadership was a great training ground for those who shared his robust instinctive approach, although it was not quite so congenial to those who had a more reflective attitude. He would never have said, with Neils Bohr: "you should regard everything I say as a question rather than an assertion." Bohr left Cambridge in 1920 to set up a new Institute in Copenhagen and in fact there was something of a divide. Rutherford and his team at the Cavendish laboratory continued to lead in experimental work, while Bohr's Institute in Copenhagen became probably the best centre in the world at that time in developing the theoretical understanding of the new physics.

Rutherford's claim to simplicity as a person is also rather misleading. Many took the face which he adopted at its face value, but one of his most gifted students, Peter Kapitsa, knew him well enough to have a greater insight. He described a more complex man in a letter to his mother in Leningrad:

"The professor is a deceptive character. They think he is a hearty colonial. Not so. He is a man of great temperament given to uncontrollable excitement. His moods fluctuate violently."

Rutherford taught and inspired a generation of physicists, many of whom were to take an important part in the development of science and its applications during the three decades after his death. As the chief founder of nuclear physics very few of his insights and predictions in this field proved to be false. One of these few was his belief that it would never be possible to release the energy locked up in the nucleus. Less than two years after his death nuclear fission was discovered (Chapter XXVI) and the race was on to find a way to harness this immense power.

(1904 – 1967)
ROBERT OPPENHEIMER – THE MANHATTAN PROJECT

No one person carries the unbearable burden of responsibility for the invention of nuclear weapons. All the necessary pieces of information were already available by 1939 and after that it was possible for any country with sufficiently advanced technology to make these weapons eventually; five countries had such projects during the Second World War.

When Rutherford showed that almost the entire mass of an atom is concentrated in an incredibly small nucleus, any scientist could see that an awesome amount of energy must be involved in holding these particles so tightly together. Some talked of finding ways of unlocking this energy, but in 1933 Rutherford explained in a public lecture that there was no practical way of doing this, and at that time all the other leading scientists agreed. When Rutherford's workers "split" atoms by bombarding them with alpha particles, more

energy was consumed than could be released. At the time there seemed no way round this, although in fact he already held one of the keys in his hand once the neutron had been discovered in 1932.

THE DISCOVERY OF FISSION

Because neutrons have no electric charge they can burrow into a nucleus with no opposition from the intense positive charge that pushes alpha particles away. Working in Rome in 1934, Enrico Fermi was the first to investigate this technique, but when he tried bombarding uranium with neutrons he got rather strange results. Like others working in this field, he was expecting that the neutrons would either knock fragments out of the nucleus (as in Rutherford's experiments), or join on to it to produce a larger atom. The nucleus itself seemed so stable that nobody even considered that it might break up. At first he thought he had managed to produce atoms of new elements, bigger than uranium, and this caused great interest among chemists. But something was not quite right, and for two or three years there was much discussion and confusion. It mattered very much to the few thousand nuclear scientists around the world, but even they would not have expected anybody else to be particularly concerned: this was still pure research.

In Berlin Otto Hahn and Lise Meitner repeated these experiments, but instead of finding the new "transuranic" elements that Fermi thought he had produced, all Hahn could find was barium. This was surprising because barium atoms are much smaller than uranium. There seemed to be no explanation unless, despite all their precautions, the original samples had been contaminated.

Hahn's assistant, Lise Meitner, was Jewish but as an Austrian she had been relatively safe so far. But while they were in the middle of these experiments she heard that German troops had marched into Austria and knew that she had to get out of Germany as quickly as possible.

In December 1938 she reached safety in Sweden. There she was met by her nephew, the physicist Otto Frisch, another refugee who was working at Neils Bohr's Institute in Copenhagen. In the course of a long walk together they inevitably discussed, among other things, Hahn's latest experiments. While they were still walking they suddenly realised what everyone else had failed to see for months: the uranium atoms were not just absorbing the neutrons, they were splitting apart into two roughly equal bits. Something quite new was happening: nuclear fission!

This was no longer just of academic interest; with war looking inevitable they could see that this had potentially very serious consequences. It opened up the possibility of producing a chain reaction which might release huge quantities of energy. When Frisch got back to Copenhagen and told Neils Bohr about their idea he immediately agreed that they must be right. Bohr himself was about to visit America and he spread the news there and also correctly predicted the way that a chain reaction could be achieved. There was great interest, and the experiments were repeated in several laboratories around the world. Soon most of those in the small world of nuclear physics realised that the genie was out of the bottle and speculations appeared in many newspapers and magazines. The technical problems would be formidable, but an atomic bomb was now a possibility to be worried about.

ON THE BRINK

In the summer of 1939, there were still many unresolved questions. Even the usually far-sighted Neils Bohr doubted whether it was an urgent problem or that it would be of relevance to the coming war. Many who knew of the new possibilities thought that the immense technical difficulties involved might give the world a twenty year breathing space. The nightmare was that it might be possible, and all the same knowledge was available in Germany where, in spite of the great outflow of refugees, there were still many scientists with the ability to take on such a project. Rudolf Peirls, another refugee from Germany who was then working in Britain recalls an important moment when he and Otto Frisch decided to try to work out the practical possibilities:

"When we sat down to consider it we found, from best estimates, that the necessary size was not tons as everybody assumed, but more like pounds [of uranium]. We also estimated what the energy released would be; we couldn't estimate it exactly but it was clearly enormous. And so we told the government immediately, because we were afraid the Nazis would get it first."

Rudolf Peirls and Otto Frisch wrote a short but very accurate outline of the practicability of making an atomic bomb. The British government took it very seriously and set up a working party, but the vast resources that would be needed ruled it out as an immediate proposition for Britain alone. America was not yet in the war and although several scientists were working on uranium, there was so far no urgency at government level. John Cockcroft, who with Ernest Walton had first split the atom, (Chapter XXV), went to America in the summer of 1940 and discussed the conclusions of Peirls and Frisch with several of the American scientists.

Einstein had already written to President Roosvelt in August 1939 about the possibility that Germany might build an atomic bomb, although he still thought that such a weapon would be far too heavy to be carried by air. With the new estimates, especially the clear, terrifying and far more urgent summary by Peirls and

The "Fat Boy" atomic bomb which devasted Nagasaki in 1945. It was almost 4 metres long, 2 metres in diameter and weighed 4500 kilograms. Together with the "Little Boy" which was dropped on Hiroshima, the bombs killed over 150,000 people.

Frisch, the decision was taken to go ahead. The United States made up for lost time by setting up what amounted to an entirely new, billion dollar industry, under the code name of "the Manhattan Project". This drew in many thousands of top level scientists from all over the world, a large proportion of them refugees from the occupied countries, with an intense personal concern that America should win this race before Nazi Germany.

THE BIRTH OF THE NUCLEAR AGE

The problem confronting them was that this was utterly new territory. In normal circumstances the new ideas and techniques would have been sifted carefully, discussed and double-checked by scientists in laboratories around the world; it would have taken many years if not decades. Now they were plunged into an unfamiliar world of military secrecy and working with a sense of life-or-death urgency. The basic ideas may have been clear, but the practical way ahead was not and there were a

few, including some high military officials, who still doubted whether it was possible at all. It was still all theory, so far nobody had even proved that a chain reaction would really happen.

Enrico Fermi, who had been in America since 1938, was the first to test this crucial point. He set up a pile of blocks of uranium and graphite in a squash court at Chicago University. Uranium naturally gives out some neutrons, and under suitable conditions these could be captured by other uranium atoms. Once captured, a target atom would break apart (fission) and in the process it would release a lot of energy – and two or three more neutrons. According to theory, provided there was enough uranium (a "critical mass") these new neutrons would each find new targets and so the process would continue, building up very rapidly as a chain reaction.

In a bomb this process had to be allowed, deliberately, to get out of control so that within a fraction of a second all the atoms in the kilogram or so or uranium

165

would break up, releasing an unimaginable amount of energy in one apocalyptic blast. In Fermi's pile this explosive build up in the number of neutrons had to be prevented. The blocks of graphite were there to slow the neutrons down, and there were also cadmium rods which absorbed neutrons, to control the reaction. On 2nd December 1942 Fermi slowly withdrew the cadmium rods and it was very soon clear that a controlled chain reaction was taking place, as predicted: the first nuclear reactor had gone critical and the nuclear age had begun.

THE MANHATTAN PROJECT

Fermi's experiment had disposed of any last real doubts that it was possible to make an atomic bomb, but there was still an argument about the most effective material to use, with some scientists supporting each of two possible routes. Natural uranium is a mixture of two different kinds of atoms; the lighter isotope, uranium 235, is the atom which has to be used for the chain reaction. But this is mixed with far more of the heavier isotope uranium 238, and to make a uranium bomb these two isotopes had to be separated. This was a difficult process which had so far only been attempted in minute amounts as a laboratory experiment. If uranium 235 was to be used to make the bomb, an entirely new technology had to be invented urgently and at once scaled up into a full manufacturing process.

The alternative to this would involve an entirely different, although an equally new and untried technology. In 1940 a group of American scientists achieved what Fermi thought he had done in 1934: they managed to build up uranium atoms into atoms with a larger nucleus. The resulting new element, plutonium, does not exist in nature, but it could be made from uranium 238 in an atomic pile. This would also be difficult, and again a wholly new manufacturing process would have to be set up. Since neither process had ever been tried and nobody could predict what snags might arise, it was decided to go ahead with both, as an insurance policy.

A third part of the project was the Los Alamos laboratory which was set up in the western desert to work on designs for the bombs and, when the uranium 238 or plutonium became available, to start building the actual weapons. Rudolf Peirls describes the group at Los Alamos.

"There were about seven thousand people living

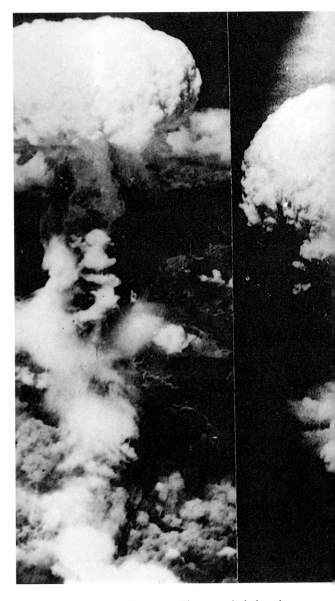

there at the end of the war. These included a few hundred very senior scientists, several Nobel Prizewinners and, apart from Americans and British, refugees from Germany, Austria, Hungary and Italy."

It would take a most unusual man to lead such a formidably talented team, which had been thrown together within a few months and which would have to work under difficult and unfamiliar conditions. The choice surprised many people: Robert Oppenheimer.

The plutonium bomb dropped on Nagasaki on 9th August, 1945. The smoke rose 6,000 metres in the air and still enveloped the city over three hours later.

J ROBERT OPPENHEIMER

Julius Robert Oppenheimer was born in New York, the son of a German immigrant who had made a fortune in the textile industry. During his undergraduate years Oppenheimer achieved excellent results in Latin and Greek as well as in his main studies, physics and chemistry. He published poetry and was also interested in oriental philosophy. After graduating from Harvard in 1925 he went on to do research in several of the European centres. He spent some time in Cambridge with Rutherford, and also worked under some of the other leading figures, such as Max Born and Neils Bohr in Germany. He was awarded his PhD at Göttingen in 1927 and returned to the United States in 1929 to take up academic posts at Berkeley and the California Institute of Technology.

He made some important contributions of his own to the developing science of nuclear physics but he became especially noted as a teacher. He had an ability to identify problems that needed to be resolved and to explain the significance of the new ideas – and was one of the first in America to see the full implications of the discovery of fission.

Although a highly gifted man, he was far less distinguished than many of the other scientists who gathered at Los Alamos to work under him. But he proved to be a good administrator and an inspiring leader of the project. Professor Freeman Dyson, who knew him well after the war, described his style:

"Suddenly he was given the chance to do something enormously important and so fascinating from a technical point of view. I think he was simply dazzled by it. He jumped at the opportunity, threw himself into it, and he made a tremendous success of it. Everybody agreed that his leadership was marvellous. He ran the thing like the conductor of a great orchestra, and it somehow ran extraordinarily smoothly because of his ability to get people to work together."

A charismatic leader was essential because the human problems of working at Los Alamos were as great as the technical demands. For security reasons it had been set up in a remote desert region in the western United States. The people working there and their families lived in fairly basic accommodation, isolated behind barbed wire fences. They were always under the tightest military security that had ever been attempted, their mail was censored and their privacy was constantly invaded. Many of them had only recently arrived as refugees in America and they were all far more used to the freedom of the international academic life than the restrictions of a top secret military operation. It was one of Oppenheimer's greatest achievements to keep morale high under these conditions.

At first it seemed to be a desperate race against time, but the threat that the Nazis would get there first gradually lessened and by the time the first bombs were being constructed it was clear that the war in Europe would soon be over. Many qualms of conscience began to trouble members of the team. Although it was entirely a national project, the team was drawn from all over the

The blighted city landscape of Hiroshima after the atomic explosion.

world and many feared the effect of giving such overwhelming power to just one country. There were also great doubts, as the first weapons were completed, whether they should actually be used or just held as a threat. There was a flurry of high level diplomatic activity, including attempts by Neils Bohr to persuade the American government to open up the project to their Russian allies. (Some had already secretly done this, as later espionage trials would show). But most of these thoughts were kept below the surface, partly by the tight security but also by the sheer momentum of the project as it began to build up to its climax.

By the summer of 1945 both the uranium 235 bomb and the plutonium bomb were almost ready. In the early hours of the morning on 16th July 1945 the first test was carried out at Alamogordo in the New Mexico desert; the plutonium device worked, and the blast was even more powerful than they had predicted.

THE AFTERMATH

Three weapons were ready, and it was now known for certain that they would have a destructive power equivalent to twenty thousand tons of conventional explosives. There were some last minute efforts to stop them being used against Japan, or at least to use one of them first as a demostration, exploding it at sea as a warning, and giving Japan the chance to surrender. The scientists were divided and even Oppenheimer, who publicly supported their use, had private doubts:

"There are passionate arguments. They do not persuade me one way or the other. At the time the alternative, the campaign of invasion, was certainly much more terrible for everyone concerned. I think that Hiroshima was far more costly in life and suffering, and inhumane, than it needed to have been, to have been an effective argument for ending the war. This is easy to say after the fact."

On 6th August 1945 the uranium bomb was dropped over Hiroshima. More than a hundred thousand people were killed instantly, and over the following months many thousands more died from their injuries or from the radiation. Three days after Hiroshima the plutonium bomb was dropped on Nagasaki with similar, terrible destruction.

THE FALL OF OPPENHEIMER

Two months later Oppenheimer resigned as the director of Los Alamos and returned to a teaching post at the California Institute. At first he remained an advisor to several government agencies, and as Chairman of the Scientific Advisory Committee for the Atomic Energy Commision, he helped to draft proposals for the international control of nuclear energy. Many were now urging that America should go on to produce the even more powerful thermonuclear weapon, the hydrogen bomb. Oppenheimer felt that this would have very serious effects on the international situation and also that the cost and technical problems involved would be excessive. He and his committee therefore advised against going ahead.

This advice was over-ruled by president Truman in 1949 and Oppenheimer's motives for his opposition were questioned; he was accused of disloyalty and of having left-wing sympathies. At a government hearing in 1954, although he was found not guilty of treason, his security

A watch caught in the blast when time stopped in Hiroshima at 2.40 pm, 6th August 1945.

Einstein and Oppenheimer in 1949. When Oppenheimer was being investigated for alleged Communist sympathies, Einstein said of him: "I admire him not only as a scientist, but also as a man of great human qualities."

clearance was removed and he was barred from all official positions.

Over the next few years he became a symbol of the witch-hunting fever that gripped America in the 1950s. Some amends were made later for his treatment when in 1963 the President conferred on him the Fermi Award for his contribution to science, on the recommendation of the Atomic Energy Commission. He spent the last few years of his life trying to resolve some of the great moral problems that face society as it comes to terms with the powers over nature that scientific discovery has given us in this century.

INDEX

dynamo 33, 38, *103*, 105
Dyson, Professor Freeman 168

earth, crust of *49*
Eastman, George 139, 140
Eastman Kodak Company 140
eclipse, solar *154-5*
Edinburgh Observatory 42
Edison, Thomas Alva 97, 100, 101-6, *102*
Edison Effect 106
Edison Swan Electric Light Company 105, 106
Ediswan lamp 105
Einstein, Albert 15, 20, 41, 46, 119, 149-56, *150, 153*, 157, 164, *170*
elasticity 121
electricity 33, 37, 38-40, 41, 44, 45, 97, 101-3, 105-6, 134
electrodes 37
electrolysis *36-7, 37*
electrolytes 37
electromagnetic field 45
electromagnetism 38, 42, 97
electrons 119, 122, 136, 152-3, 158, 159, 160-1
elements
    Aristotle's four 31-2
    atomic weights of 158
    chemical 31-2
Elements of Chemistry, The (Lavoisier) 158
Elements of Geology (Lyell) 49
Elizabeth I, Queen 9, 10, 14
EMI Marconi 136
Endeavour 66
energy, transfers of 43-4
"ether" 44, 45, 154
Euclid 146
evolution, theory of 52, 54, 56-8, 61, 64
Experiment with the Air Pump (Wright) *23*
Experimental Researches in Electricity (Faraday) 38
Experiements and Observations on Different Kinds of Air (Priestley) 24-5

Faraday, James 33
Faraday, Margaret 33
Faraday, Michael 33-40, *34, 35*, 42, 45, 97, 101, 105, 121, 158
Faraday's Laws 37-8
"Fat Boy" atomic bomb *165*
fermentation 70, 72
Fermi, Enrico 163, 164, 165
Fernseh AG 135
fibre optics 133, 138
flask, swan-necked *70*, 70-1
Fleming, Sir Alexander 75-80
Florey, Haward Walter, Baron 75, 80
fluroscence 123

Flyer 3 108-9
Flyer, The 109-12
flying machines 107-12
Ford, Edsel *117*
Ford, Henry 113-18, *114-5, 117*
Ford Foundation 118
Form Motor Company 116
fossils 49, 51, 52, 53-4, 56, 58
    fossil shell *chara 50*
Franklin, Benjamin 21, 38
French Revolution 26, 27, 52, 69
Fresnel, Augustin 152
friction 32
Frisch, Otto 164, 165

Galapagos Islands Finches 56
    sea lizard 57
Galilei, Galileo 14, 18
gangrene 78
gases 22-4, 27, 32, 43
    kinetic theory of 151
Geiger, Hans 159
General Theory 155
genetic engineering 64
genetics 59, 64, 100
Geological Society 52
geology 47-52, 53-4, 61
geometry 146
George III, King 26
Gillray, James 67
glaciers 48, 52
gliders 107-9, 134
Grainger, Percy 144
gramophone 100, 104, 144
gravitation, theory of 15, 17-19, *18-19*
gravity, law of 45
Gray, Elisha 97, 99
Great Eastern (steam ship) 97
Great Western Railway 90, 94
Grey, Charles, 2nd Earl 93
Grey, Thomas 90
gunpowder 10, 81

Hahn, Otto 164
Halley, Edmund 16, 19
Harvey, William 14
heat 14, 32, 44, 121
Hedley, William 87, 90
Heisenberg, Werner 153
Helmholtz, Hermann von 119
Henry, Joseph 97
Herapath, 43
heredity, theory of 63-4
Herschel, Sir John 58
Hertz, Heinrich Rudolf 45
high-voltage accelerator 162
Hiroshima 156, *168-9*, 171
Hodges, Dr Andrew 143

Hooke, Robert 16, 18
horsepower, unit 86
Hunter, John 66
Huskisson, William 93-4
Hutton, James 48-9
Huxley, Thomas Henry 58
Huygens, Christiaan 19, 20, 81
Hyatt, John 139
hybridisation 61, 64
hydrofoils 100
hydrogen 22, 29, 32, 159
    bomb 171
hydrogen chloride 24

immunisation 74
immunology 69
Industrial Revolution 81, 86, 95
inertia 17
inoculation 65-6, 67-8 *see also* vaccination
Inquiry into Cause and Effects of the Variolae Vaccinae, An (Jenner) 68
Instauratio Magna (Bacon) 12
ions 37

Jacquard, Joseph Marie 143-4
James I, King 10, 11-12
James II, King 20
Jeans, Sir James 120
Jenner, Catherine 68
Jenner, Edward 65-8, 73
Johannsen, Wilhelm Ludwig 64
Johnson, Samuel 26

Kapitsa, Peter 162
Kelvin, William Thomson, 1st Baron 58, 159
Kepler, Johann 9, 17, 18
Kinetoscope Parlour 106
Kitty Hawl, North Carolina 109

Lamarck, Jean Baptiste, Chevalier de 54
lamp (light bulb), electric 103, *103*, 105-6
Langley, Samuel 112
laser beams 100
Lauder, J.E. 84
Laue, Max von 122-3
Lavoisier, Antoine-Laurent 24, 26, 27-32, *31*, 38, 158
Lavoisier, Madame 28, *31*, 32
Lavoisier's Principle (conservation of matter, law of) 30
leeches 66
Leibniz, Gottfried Wilhelm 16
Lenin, V.I. 118
Leonardo da Vinci 107
Leucippus 158
Life of Johnson (Boswell) 26
light 24, 41, 42, 44, 45

PICTURE CREDITS

Energy Authority: 160, 161

Bodleian Library: 131

Bridgeman Art Library (Royal Society): 157

Broadside Archives: 13, 16, 17, 30, 43, 49, 50, 60, 70, 141, 147

Cambridge University Library: 44

Jean-Loup Charmet: 124

Culver Pictures: 33, 53, 69, 95, 101, 110, 113, 117, 126, 139, 149, 150

E.T. Archive: 62, 67, 81, 107, 114, 136

Mary Evans Picture Library: 35, 55, 57, 58, 102, 104, 126

Henry Ford Museum: 116

Fotomas: 11, 56

Michael Holford: 18, 22, 28, 36, 39, 87(L), 99, 103

Mansell Collection: 27, 72-3, 76, 82, 92, 96, 97, 98, 111, 119, 120-1, 122-3

Marconi: 127, 128, 130

Museum of Modern Art, N.Y.: 31

National Archive for the History of Computing: 144, 146

National Gallery, London: 23

National Gallery of Scotland: 84

N.P.G., London: 9, 15, 21, 41, 47, 65, 87(R)

Pasteur Institute: 71

Popperfoto: 133, 134, 135, 137, 151, 153, 163, 165, 166-7, 169, 170

The Royal Institution: 34

St. Mary's Medical School: 75

Science Museum, London: 25, 29, 46, 83, 85, 88-9, 91, 93, 108-9, 126(R)

Science Photo Library: 19, 63, 78, 79, 154, 158-9

Topham Picture Library: 171

Cover Pictures:

Top Row: N.P.G., Science Photo Library, N.P.G.

Middle Row: Broadside Books Archives, Science Photo Library

Bottom Row: N.P.G., Science Photo Library, Bridgeman Art Library

End papers: Popperfoto